Folk Tales of Liberia

"In *Folk Tales of Liberia*, the authors have preserved the spirit and the thought purpose in the original as nearly as is possible to literature transferred to another language. I congratulate them for this good translation which is sure to arouse the interest of the reading public in the wealth of Liberian tribal folklore and culture."

—HON. OSCAR S. NORMAN,

> *Assistant Secretary of the Interior of Liberia, In Charge of the Department of Folkways*

FOLK TALES OF LIBERIA

by J. LUKE CREEL

In collaboration with Mr. Bai Gai Kiahon
of the Vai Tribe in Liberia

Illustrations by CAROL HOORN FRASER

Publishers

T. S. Denison & Co., Inc.

Minneapolis

Contents

TO THE READER

These stories that have been passed down orally from generation to generation are, for the most part, common to Africa in varying versions. The tales used here are from the Vai Tribe of Liberia, the tribe of which the narrator of these stories is a native. In translating these stories into English the reader will gain a knowledge of the rich folklore of Liberia, a country that has long been of special interest historically to the American government and the American people. Therefore, no deviations from the original of these stories in plot, thought and purpose have been made.

The authors have made use of both conventional and colloquial English in an attempt to retain for the reader, as much as possible, the mood and flavor contained in the original tales without, at the same time, precluding a translation interesting to the general public. Hence, this collection is not intended as a sourcebook for specialized study in anthropological and sociological research. If these stories prove of value to any kind of specialized study, that result will be one in addition to that which the compilers had intended or expected.

That is to say again that the purpose of the collectors of these tales has been to make a book intelligible and appreciable to the general reading public. Some original flavor has, of course, been sacrificed. For, when retention of that flavor is the prime purpose of the translator of African folk tales, the result is almost sure to be either dullness or a sort of foreign novelty which soon loses its appeal as novelties always do. Such translations are of interest and value to specialized study. This collection is intended to appeal to a larger audience without sacrificing the original story and its purpose (each tale intends a moral) and with retaining as much as is possible in this type of translation the mood, feeling, and flavor peculiar to the ethnic languages of Africa.

7

1) the importance of the dead in life (has a role in life
   thru other shapes

2) insistance on peace in the world.

3) equality (even slaves are free), justice, sharing

4) Freedom of women

THE DESERTED CHILD

Once there was a rich African and he had many wives. He had everything. His wives and children and servants made a whole village and it was removed from other villages, and they were all rich because he was rich and they were all free, even the servants felt free, and they were all happy, and they had peace.

But one day he died. All at once he died. And the wives wailed and the servants moaned, and nobody knew what to do—not the women, not the servants. And the servants ran away and joined other masters, to be directed by a living master; they would not serve a dead master. And the wives talked together. They looked at each other and didn't cry any more. They talked together and they said, "Why should we stay here? He has gone. We are alone. There is no man here. Why should we stay here? This wealth is nothing now. Everything is here but it is nothing. Let's go back to our homes, each to her family. Back where there are men. He is dead. He is gone." And they all left. All but one.

One lingered and wept and said, "I cannot go. My womb is heavy. I will bear this child here, for he is dead that got him and is buried here. I will stay here." And she bowed her head and was silent. And the others said, "We are sorry for you. You are big with the dead man. He will not rise for his child. Go back to your village. Your parents will receive you." And they chanted together.

9

Leave the dead behind.
The dead are too much dead.
The dead are too much alive!
Welcome the living alive.
Welcome the dead that are dead.
But the dead are too much alive!

And they left her, looking back over their shoulders, but she did not follow. They vanished out of sight, this way and that way, and she was alone in the lonely village with the empty huts and the empty wealth and the dreary day and the lonely night. And after three dreary days and three lonely nights she wept again and said, "I cannot bear it alone. I will go back to life, back to my parents, back to my people," and she turned her back on the lonely, empty village and walked a long, lonely distance and came in sight at last of her native village which was on a little hill. But when she started up the hill to the village a great pain came into her womb each time she tried to set a foot forward. She could not walk another foot forward. At last she turned back and all at once the pain went away and she could walk. She was glad. She turned again to walk up to the village but the pain struck greatly again and she could not move a foot before her. She turned again in the direction of her husbands' village and the pain was gone and she could walk. But she tried again and many times to go up the hill but the pain would not let her.

The dead are so much alive!

"My husband does not want it so," she said, and she trekked the long, lonely way back to the lonely, empty village. And there she passed many days. Days ran after days and finally her time came and she had no help, and a strange thing happened. A gentle cow was still in the village and that cow came forward and did strange things, for whatever the woman needed the cow supplied, some way moved things to her, somehow supplied. By and by the woman could take care of herself and the little son she bore, but still

the cow did strange things. Strange and helpful things. And when the baby was no more a little baby, when the baby was now a child the woman said, "Now, I'll go back to my people. With my little son I'll go back to my people." And after many days she came to the hill where the village was. But when she started to climb the hill something happened to the boy's neck and his neck was as a broken neck. The moan from her heart came out from her lips and she turned to go to a smooth place to lay him down, but as she turned back, the boy was all at once well again. She was glad and said, "It was just the heat that did it. It was just the heat." She started again to ascend the hill but at once the boy's neck was as a broken neck, and when she turned with him back he was at once all whole again. She wept and said, "Alas, the Dead will not have it so." And she wept some more and prayed and went sorrowfully the long journey back to the lonely, empty village. Day gave chase to day and the little boy grew but the mother pined and nearly went out of mind from loneliness. And one day she ran away fast from the village, ran away fast from the child, and all the distance back to her father's place she ran away fast from her thoughts. And her people received her with joy and tears, for she wept out the sad story of her loss and her lonely grief, but she did not tell of the child. She ran away far from her thoughts, so far she ran right into love again and she married, and she buried the past and was happy, and she bore a daughter. And there was life there in that village, there were people there. She was not lonely. And day ran after day.

And back in the lonely village, back in the forgotten village the cow came forward and somehow, some way helped the child. And the child knew the language of the cow and the cow knew the language of the child. And there was personality in the cow that was not strange to the child, and the child and the cow conversed. And day followed day till the child was no more a child. He was a young man, tall and elegant his body, shining ebony his countenance, a tree of shining ebony under the African sun. And he conversed with the cow, and his understanding was great.

Finally one day came a caravan, a great caravan to the village bound on a long journey. And the leaders talked to the boy and begged to stay the night in the village, to stay for rest, for comforting, restoring rest. "Who are you? Where have you come from? Where are you going?" The tall young man asked questions and looked the strangers in the face. "We are traders," said the strangers. "We are traders bound for the East to sell slaves for much money and many ornaments. And all these men and women with us are slaves, strong as beasts, swift as birds. They will make us rich. Let us pass the night. There are many huts here and no people here. We will give money, we will give gifts. Let us pass the night."

"Wait," said the boy. "Wait till I return," and he disappeared

and sought the cow and consulted with the cow. And he said, "I want the slaves, the handsome men in bonds, the beautiful women in bonds." And the cow made him understand all the wealth that was his, the locked-up huts that were filled with money, the locked-up huts that were filled with jewels, the locked-up huts that were filled with rings and beads. Then he knew how rich he was and his heart leaped up with joy and his jubilant feet moved fast. "You can stay for the night," he announced to the strangers, "but you must sell to me the slaves, the men, the women and the children all. What do you want for the slaves?" "We want money, we want some jewel-stones, we want some rings and we want some many-colored beads."

"How much?" said the rich young man, and the strangers told him. He said, "You will stay the night with me, and tomorrow I will buy your slaves," and he opened to them many huts and they spread their beds on the floor.

Then the sun returned and scattered the night, and he brought the money and the jewel-stones, the rings and the beads from the locked-up huts, and he made the traders glad to go to their homes again and leave him all the slaves.

Then he broke the bonds of the slaves and made them freemen of his village. Then there was life again, lively life in the village, sounds of laughter, dance and song. For there was plenty there— wealth and freedom and peace and joy. And day followed day.

And the mother, where was she? One day with her daughter she went to visit a farm, by a round-about road she went to visit a farm and she ended near the very same village, but she knew not where she was. And to the farm came sounds floating upon the wind, sounds of music and laughter, dance and song. Blended merriment floated upon the wind. And the mother said, "Let us go where the merriment is," and she walked with her daughter to the village, but she knew not where she was. The village was fresh and new all over, and she knew not where she was, but she joined with her daughter in the merriment and wished she lived in a village of so much life and free-time joy. Then she saw the chief, the handsome chief, the countenance-shining chief, and she felt a pang in the heart, the pang of love in the heart.

The dead are so much alive!

She forgot the husband she had and yearned for the rich young chief, forgot the age she was and yearned for the glittering chief, and she spoke to him what her heart compelled.

But when he could do it with ease the young chief imparted to the cow the presence of the strange woman and the strange words of the strange woman. And the cow made the young man this to know: "That strange woman is your mother and that young girl is your sister." And the youth was astounded, but the cow made him to know the whole story from beginning to end and the youth listened with wonderment. Then he went to the mother and revealed himself, and the mother was humbled and wept and begged forgiveness. But he raised her up and made a feast and prepared a place, a special home for his mother there and for his sister and sent for the stepfather to join them there.

And finally he took a wife, the daughter, the stately daughter of one of the freemen whose freedom from the traders he purchased,

whose bonds he broke. And there was feasting and mirth. Sounds of music and dance and song blended together and floated upon the wind. For all were joy - makers there, and there were no servants there, yet all were servants there, for all each other served. And day ran after day, but pleasure ran no other where, and there was work and there was play, and there was peace.

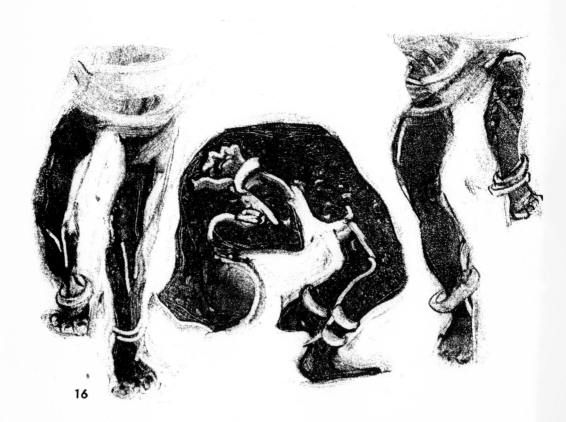

THE SHINING
STRANGER

He was not a chief but he was a rich man and he had two wives that loved him. But one was selfish. She thought only of herself and her daughter. The other wife also had a daughter but she was thoughtful of other people, even of the other wife and her daughter. She treated the daughter of the other wife as if she were her daughter too. But the selfish wife was jealous of the thoughtful wife and of her daughter and she loathed both the mother and the daughter, for the daughter had virtues like the virtues of her mother, and she was known and loved far and near. But the daughter of the jealous wife was full of the selfishness of her mother. She too was known, and because she was known she was not loved as was her sister.

Now one day there came to the village a shining stranger. He was majestic. Nobody had seen a man like him. He was handsome, he was beautiful, majestic his form, beautiful his manly face, wonderful his personality. There was a light shining out of him like from a god hiding inside. Nobody knows what is hiding in a man. Maybe a god; maybe a demon. Nobody knows. But a big light comes out of some men, and out of this man there came a big light. And the men admired him—yes, and they envied him, and the girls lost their hearts. He was kind to them all, polite to them all, but he sought always the virtuous daughter of the virtuous mother. And everyone said, "Who is this man? What kind of man is this man? Where has this man come from?" But the man only said he was

17

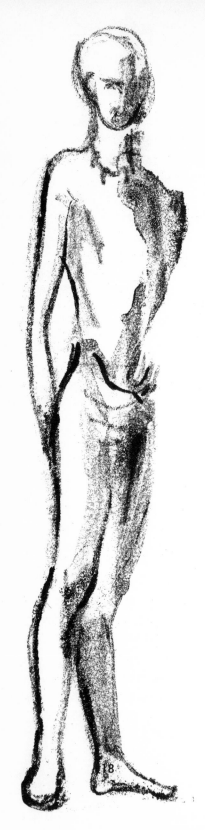

from a foreign land. He said he was traveling to see strange lands, and he would soon go back to his own land.

But he didn't go back at once. He walked and talked and sat with the virtuous daughter of the virtuous mother. And the daughter begged the shining stranger never to leave, never to go back again to his far-away land, begged him to stay in the land of her father. But he said he could not stay. He must return to the far-away land, the land that was his land, the land that must be always his land. But she said she could not part from his side. "I will go where you go," she said. "I will go to a land that is new to me. I will go to a land that is strange to me. I will go by your side. By your side I will stay."

And he said, "You do not know what you do. You will go far, far away from your land, far away from your father, far away from your mother, and long is the returning. It may not be as you think in that land, it may not be as you wish, and long is the returning."

But she said, "I will stay at your side. I do not seek great pleasure. I do not ask for pleasant ease. I do not crave great riches. I crave only to be at your side. I shall lack naught if I be at your side. All will be mine if I be at your side."

And the shining stranger said, "It shall be so."

The day came for them to depart and the

mother embraced her and wept; the father embraced her and groaned. For all seemed strange and unknown. The shining stranger was still strange, strange and unknown. Their daughter was going to a land strange and unknown, and the mother wept and the father groaned. But the daughter smiled and was happy, and with light heart and light feet she left with the shining stranger. The jealous mother did not weep. She was mad and she was glad. Mad because the girl had the beautiful stranger; glad because the girl was going away. "She will die," she said to her daughter, "she will die on the way to that far-away land. She will not return here. I am glad."

So the shining stranger led the virtuous daughter away and they traveled a very great distance but she did not grow tired. And the girl said, "Tell me. How shall I act in your land? That I may soon become part of that land, how shall I speak, what shall I do?" And the stranger said, "Remember this: *Speak little. Do much.* Remember only this. Remember it well." And he said no more. And the words sank deep in her heart and were graven on her mind.

At last they came to high mountains. On the straight, level land high mountains stood up with their heads in the clouds. And there the stranger stopped and stood still. And from somewhere above, so high above she could not see, a great chain came down. And on the end of the chain was a platform like a floor, and the

platform rested on the earth and was still. Then the stranger stepped upon the platform and sat down. Then he said, "Come, sit by my side," and she sat by his side and she did not fear. The stranger smiled but he did not speak, and they traveled up, up, by the high, high, mountains.

At last they stopped and again they were on broad, level land. It was a beautiful land. Palm trees and green grass and bright flowers and cool breezes. It was a beautiful land. And she heard soft, beautiful voices greeting her, and music as of many instruments, but she saw nobody. She was filled with wonder and question but she said nothing, for she remembered the stranger's words: *Speak little. Do much.* Then said the shining stranger, "Whatever you need in this land it will be immediately supplied." Then he said, "Come," and they walked upon soft grass under palm trees fanned by cool breezes to the stranger's fair palace.

Then he said, "I want you to come to my mother. I want you to meet my mother." And he led her to a room where was his mother lying sick on a bed, her legs covered with festerous sores. There was an offensive stench from the sores, and the room was filled with the stench. But the heart of the girl was filled with compassion for the suffering woman, and she got a basin of water and washed with loving care the diseased limbs and applied salving balms, and this she did day after day. And the woman was grateful and she loved the virtuous girl, and for her bespoke blessings day by day.

And the shining stranger smiled. He was pleased. And all her wants were supplied. If she said, "I am thirsty," cool water was set before her but she saw not the hands that placed it there. If she said, "I am hungry," a feast was immediately spread before her, but she saw nobody, and she asked no questions.

Then after a long, long time the girl began to yearn to see her parents. She was not tired of the beautiful land, she was not tired of the sick, sick mother and the offensive, sickly odor and the unsightly sores. She only yearned to see her parents, to embrace them once again. And the shining stranger said, "It shall be so. Long is the returning, but it shall be so. Whether you can return here, that is a question. Whether you can return to your parents, that is not a question. It shall be so."

Then she told to the sick mother that she was going to her own land far, far away to see her parents. And the mother said, "You have been very good to me; you have been faithful without compulsion, for nothing was required," and she bespoke blessings upon the journey. And the girl once more laved tenderly the sore limbs

and applied the salving balms. Then the mother said, "I have information and advice before you go. My son will set out for you several boxes. One of those boxes you can choose to take with you as a gift to your home. No girl goes from her new home back to her parents without bearing a gift. There will be gold boxes, there will be silver boxes, boxes studded with diamonds, others with sapphire, and still others with other kinds of rare stones. But I advise you to

pass them by and choose the little wooden box, the ugly little wooden box for your own. A little black cat will be sitting on the box and you cannot miss it. I advise you to take that box." The virtuous girl said, "It shall be so."

And the boxes were there as the woman had said, beautiful and tempting. But she passed them by and chose the wooden box that looked to be nothing, and she knew it was the one, for a little black cat was perched on the box, licking its paw and washing its face. And said the shining stranger, "Is that the box you want?" And she said, "Yes." He said, "Are you sure you want that mean little box?" She said, "This one I choose," and he said, "It shall be yours." Then he led her to the place where was the platform and the chain without end, and she seated herself and he bade her good-by, and she disappeared far, far below.

And when she arrived from the long, long journey at the home of her parents there was much joy, and she talked of the beauty of that far-away land and they listened with wonder, but she did not tell all. And they asked, "What gift have you borne from that beautiful land?" She pointed to the box and said, "We will see." Then she opened the box and a great miracle was performed. A whole city issued from the box and spread itself out on the unpeopled land, a city of fair, bright buildings, not a city of mean, ugly huts. And there were provided musicians and everything to make it a city of joy, and everybody was in great delight and they all praised the virtuous daughter.

But in her own house, the same village house, the jealous wife sulked with her daughter. She began to complain to the daughter. "Why do you not do something," she said, "why do you not find a man from a new land and bring back wonderful gifts?" And at that time the shining stranger appeared in that part of the village, and he talked with the daughter of the jealous mother. He did not enter the fair bright city, just talked with the daughter in the village. And the daughter said, "I wish to go away with you. I wish to go to your land. I wish to be with you. Take me to your land." And the stranger said, "The way is far and the journey is difficult. Maybe you cannot endure that journey with me." She said, "I will go," and the stranger said, "It shall be so." Then the mother was glad, she was filled with glee, and she told the daughter to come back fast from that land, to come back fast with rich gifts, to outdo by far her sister. And the daughter said, "It shall be so."

But all the way she complained of the journey and asked many questions about the new land. He answered only, "When you come to that land remember this, remember only this: *Speak little. Do much.*" Then they came to the platform and the chain and sat down, and immediately they began to rise. She asked, "Where does this chain come from? How long is this chain? How far do we go?" He did not answer and she was peeved. Then finally they stopped in that beautiful land and she heard soft, beautiful voices welcoming her. She said, "Whose voices are these? I see nobody. Explain this to me." He did not answer and she was displeased. Then she said, "I am thirsty," and immediately cool water was placed before her, but she saw nobody. She said, "I don't know whether I should drink this water, for I did not see the hands that brought it. Maybe they are dirty hands that brought this water." He said, "You are safe," and she drank the water. Then she said, "I am hungry," and a full feast was spread before her. She said, "How can I eat this food when I saw not the hands that prepared it?" He said, "It is good," and she ate like one half afraid.

Then they walked on the soft grass beneath the swaying palms to his fair palace. Then he said, "I have a sick mother. She is sadly afflicted. I hope you will be kind to my sick mother." She said, "Well, if she is pleasant to know I will be so." And he led her to the sick mother. She said, "This is a horrid stench. Do not expect me to stay in this room. This is a horrid stench." And each day she came but would not enter the room. She said, "Get you a servant. I am not a servant." And it was soon that she asked to go home. "It shall

be so," said the shining stranger. "Long is the way but you will arrive." Then she stood outside the room and told the sick mother she was going home. And the mother said, "You have not been good to me, no salving balm for my sores, no gentle washing of my limbs. But I wish you good journey, and I give you good advice before you go." Then she told her of the boxes, and told her to choose the mean, little box just as she had advised the virtuous sister. But the moment the girl saw the boxes she said, "I don't know why I should take a dirty wooden box when I can have a fine box," and she chose a gold box studded with bright jewels. The stranger said, "Is that the one you want?" She said, "This is the box." He said, "Are you sure you want that one?" She said, "I know which box I want. This is my box." He said, "It shall be so." Then he led her to the broad platform and she seated herself with the box and disappeared far, far below.

When she arrived home her mother was gleeful. The box was a treasure-gift even if it were empty. The mother said, "We were

25

not present when your sister opened her box. They shall not see you open your treasure. But call in all of my people." And the daughter did so, and everybody waited to see what sort of great miracle would be performed for them. She opened the box and there on top was a richly shining spread. "This," she said, "shall be a gift for my mother," and the mother received it gleefully. Then there was another rich cloth, which she started to lift up. "This," she said—but she said no more, for a hideous miracle occurred. From under that spread issued lions, tigers, leopards, crocodiles and giant snakes, and they devoured the whole company. Then the box and all that came with it disappeared.

But the bright city remained bright and joyful, and the name given it means (though few people know this today) THE BRIGHT CITY. It is an ancient city now, but you can see it for yourself if you travel long enough in Africa.

THE HANDSOME YOUNG MAN

Too much beauty has often become an inconvenience to the man or woman who possesses it. And that is what this story is about.

There was a young man living once in the capital town of an African tribe, and his beauty was such that every woman who saw him, the married and the unmarried, wanted him for her own, and wherever he went he was like a city besieged. Heaven, it seemed, had been prodigal in blessing or cursing, him with beauty so great, and at times he himself wondered whether his beauty were a blessing or a curse. The women did not swoon when they saw him. They woke up. For he did not possess one kind of beauty only, like beauty of body, or beauty of face, or beauty of manner, or brightness of mind, any one of which in abundance is about as much as a person can conveniently carry. But this young man had all in abundance. He had everything. And the women woke up. Wherever he went the women woke up.

Now among the wakeful ones who had seen him was the wife of the king. She came to him secretly, she made love to him secretly, she spent time with him secretly. It was a wrong to the king; it was falseness and shame; but she was a victim, she said, of the young man's beauty; it could not be helped. She excused herself thus and felt then no shame, and by stealth she continued to see the young man.

But finally the king became suspicious. There was something strange, he thought, about his wife. She was not interested in him any more. She was not interested in the court any more. Her mind was occupied with something unknown. What could it be? The king grew suspicious and he set watchers, secret watchers, to watch. Then secret watchers of the wife reported to her that she was discovered by the king's secret watchers, and she ran fast to the young man and said they were discovered and the king would put them to death. Then they fled in the darkness together, hoping to reach the far-away border and enter another land and find shelter from death. The way was long and escape would be difficult, for they knew the king's men would pursue them.

Then deep in the night the king went to his wife's bedchamber and she was not there. "She is now with the young man. I shall take them together. This is as I wanted. I shall take them together. Together they shall die." And he went with his strong men to the young man's dwelling to slay them together, but the dwelling was vacant and his purpose was foiled. Then to his anger was added more anger, because his purpose was foiled. He had been tasting of mad satisfaction. He was ready to eat and to swallow satisfaction, and the table had vanished before him. But he swore they would not escape, and in every direction he sent pursuers with sharp, hungry swords. They should not escape.

The next day as the day was beginning to wane, the fleeing pair had grown weary from swift flight without rest, and finally the false wife grew faint without rest, without food, and without drink. Then they met the wife of a farmer with a basket of food, going to her husband in the field with a basket of food, to feed the famished husband toiling in the field. Then the fleeing wife said, "Oh, sell us this food. We must have this food. We are dying for food. I will make gifts, rich gifts for your food." The other woman answered, "I cannot give this food. My husband is hungry and weak for this food. This food is for him, no other may have it."

Then she looked for the first time at the fair, handsome youth, and her heart fled her body, and she forgot her husband toiling in the field. And she said, "Share with me your husband. You shall have all this food. I wish to join you forever and share with you this husband." And the other said, "Nay, nay! Here are rich gifts. Accept these rich gifts." But the other would not bargain. She had but one price. The famished wife could not go on without food and without drink, and soon the pursuers would take them. And she thought, "What matters it? Somehow we shall lose her when the escape has been made." Then they took all the food and the drink and were strengthened, and the three fled fast before the pursuers.

At last they came to a river, a swift-current river, and there on the brink of the swift-current river was a canoe, and in the canoe a woman was sitting as if patiently waiting. There was no other crossing, no other canoe at that far isolation. And the first wife spoke: "Bear us across this swift-current river. Here are rich gifts. Bear us quickly across." But the woman said, "I cannot move this canoe.

I await now for my husband. I cannot be absent the moment he arrives." Then the young man said, "We are hotly pursued; our lives are in danger. Row us across and spare us this death!" And as he spoke the woman looked at him and rose up like one in a hurry and she forgot then her husband. And she said, "Be also my husband! I will go with you; I will join you forever. Be also my husband." But the first wife groaned and cried, "Nay, nay! Accept these rich gifts." But the youth looked over his shoulder and saw in the distance fast-moving pursuers, and the bargain was made.

Then they crossed in a hurry the swift-current river. And the pursuers came and could not cross at once the swift-current river, and at last, weary and faint, the young man and the three women crossed the border into the land of the neighboring tribe and there begged for shelter and succor. Strong tribesmen listened to the pleas of the strangers and said: "Have you not heard of our king, of his treatment of strangers, the test he applies to all strangers, the death that comes of the failure to answer the question he gives them? Have you not heard?" And they answered, "We know not of this."

Then the strong tribesmen led them to the king and the king said to the young man, "You and these women shall live if you answer the question I give you. You see that I am very rich and my kingdom is prosperous and my people contented. What is the secret, what is the source of my wealth? Answer this question and live. All other strangers that came here have died. You, too, have life or death for reward. And my throne he inherits who answers this question. How long will you live? How soon will you die? Come back here tomorrow to live or to die." He called to the guards to bear them away.

Then he turned to his daughter, his beautiful daughter he loved more than his wealth. Why was she trembling, what illness had seized her? She said she was not well and begged to go to her chamber. And the king called for attendants and sent the princess to her chamber. Then she sent them away. But she did not lie down. She paced fast the floor and her thoughts raced with her heart, and her heart raced so hard she could not control well her thoughts. But the soft twilight becalmed her, and she made a resolve. No fear should deter her, no allegiance to father, no love that she bore him. This new love henceforth should guide and control her; henceforth forever, only this love.

And in the dark of the night she stole to the place where the young man was kept, stole past the guards and came to his side, as quiet as a ghost she slid to his side. He lay wide awake; his mind was a work-house, and sleep fled him afar. And with surprise he beheld her. She seemed not to arrive. She seemed only to be there. How long had she been there? His lips parted to speak, but she stopped fast the words with her lips on his lips. Then she told him to speak not, to utter no word, but only to listen. And she whispered her love, her undying love; and the secret she gave him that would give to him life and the throne of her father. Then she begged him to remember and to take her for wife; then the chaste princess kissed him and left him and returned to her chamber. But he did not sleep. He lay wide awake with love in his heart—love for her beauty, but

most for her chastity. She was not like the others. She was beautiful and chaste, and he lay wide awake with love in his heart.

The next day a crowd had assembled. And when they saw the young man they wished he might live. So much beauty, they said, ought to live. Such excellence ought not to die. Many wished that they knew then the answer. They would save that excellence from death. They would keep that excellent one for king when the rich king into death's land had journeyed. But only the king knew the answer, and sadly they waited the doom of the youth. And they praised the courage of the youth, the calm, the quiet demeanor. They heard the king call for the answer and saw the youth walk back and forth pondering hard the question.

At last he walked straight to the king, caught firmly the cane of the king, the beautiful cane of the king and spoke clearly in tones they could hear. "Your cane, O great king, is a magical cane. This cane is the source of your wealth. May it never be lost to your kingdom. May this magic abide here forever." And the king arose with a shout and said: "This is the man Heaven has sent. This is your leader in the day that I leave you. Salute now the leader of that day when I leave you." And a thousand throats became vocal and a shout went up to the sky, and spears went high above heads, and for three days there was holiday feasting, and music and dance and song.

But in life one problem gives place to another. The king told him to choose him a wife to sit in honor beside him, to fulfill the tribal custom and choose a wife thus to honor. And the three women who came with him each pressed hard her right to the honor. The first said she had lost her king and her kingdom, and all for the love that she bore him. The second said she had given him life with the food of her husband; he would have perished but for the food that she gave him; and the third said she had saved him and saved all from the swordsmen when she rowed them across the swift-current river. The poor princess could not press her cause as could these aloud in the open, but she begged him alone in secret, and his mind was again like a workshop.

He was like a city besieged—just as before. Which one should he choose? Which one did he take? Decide for yourselves. Converse well together and decide for yourselves.

THE PRINCESS AND THE PRISONER

There was a king in a part of Africa and he had many subjects, and riches like a king, and many wives. But he had only one child and that child was a daughter. You can imagine how he loved that daughter, but you can't understand how he treated her and you can't understand why. He didn't want her to know men—that is, young men; not until she was very mature in years did he want her to know men. She was to rule the kingdom with the man that became her husband. So the man that took her for his would become a king and he would really be IT, he would be the ruler, the real ruler. So the king, her father, wanted her to choose well, and he thought to keep her away from men till she was grown in prudence, and from the time she was a small child she didn't know boys.

Her house and the grounds took up much space and she could walk and run and stroll and play. She had everything there, but all was sealed off from the rest of the world. Yet she didn't know that; she did not know the world, and so she was happy. The king visited his daughter and she thought all men were like her father and the old men who were servants there. But mainly the servants surrounding her were women and they were all faithful to the wishes of the king. And so the little princess had everything but little boys to play with, and when she became a young woman she had every-

thing but young men. But for awhile she didn't know that, and so for awhile she was happy.

Now it happened that near the grounds of the princess there was a prison, and in that prison there was a young man not like anybody else in that prison. He was not a criminal. He had committed only a minor offense, but he was poor and insignificant, and so he was forgotten, and he languished in the prison more than two years. But he had much spirit, he had enterprise, he could not be forever still, and so he managed little by little to make a hole in the roof above his narrow room. A long time and much careful work it cost him. But one day—how glad he was to see the blue sky! And then when he climbed out onto the roof he found that he could not easily be seen from that part of the roof. The day would come, he thought, when he could climb down and run away. Run far away, to a far-away place, across the hot sands to a far-away place, to a deep, cool forest in a far-away place, to run and leap and to throw the spear and to swim the stream in the deep, cool forest, and to laugh and laugh in the warm, bright sun, in the warm, bright sun in a far-away place. But now he looked about him to learn well the land around him and the best ways for his escape, but he didn't look long, for he was afraid, and so he crept back and covered the hole so nobody could see that a hole was once there. The next day he crawled out again and stayed longer.

So it went day after day, and each day he looked down into the private gardens of the Princess, the spacious, private gardens of the Princess, the park-like gardens of the Princess. Always he wondered and pondered in his mind what that great place might be. He saw people working and moving about in the quiet, walled-in place,

36

and one day finally he saw the Princess, and love made a nest in his heart. Deep in his heart love made a nest and sat there like a bird. But he said nothing then. Not then, but there was another day. And on that day she bathed in a basin in the garden, in the garden she bathed in a basin, made fresh her limbs in the garden, in the basin her ebony limbs, and none might see in the garden, but the youth on the roof looked down, down on the Princess in the garden, bathing in a basin in the garden; and he made a cry like pain, and the Maiden looked up from the garden. O, on that day! The Maiden looked up from the garden and love made a nest in her heart, deep

in her heart love made a nest and sat there like a bird. He was not like her father. He was not like the servant men. And now she knew. All at once she knew. She knew there were men not like her father. She knew there were men not like the servants. She knew there were men. And this one was hers. Let down from heaven and fallen on a roof! She stretched her arms and her arms said, "Come." She lifted her arms and her arms said, "Take me." And love found a way.

Love climbs walls. Love pierces walls. Love breaks prisons, makes holes in prisons and hides the holes. In the cool, dark night he got into the garden and the Princess watched and met him half way. And the beautiful Princess and the handsome prisoner were melted as one by love. But not till later did he know she was the Princess, and not till later did she know he was a prisoner, but he could not love her more because she was the Princess, and she could not love him less because he was the prisoner. Their love was that full. To the garden he stole and back to the prison, time after time, time after time, and love made them as man and wife.

Finally the Princess bore a son, and the king was a puzzled man, but the Princess would not explain. She said, "Man? What man? What do you say?" For awhile the king tried to believe in miracles because he wanted now to believe in miracles. But the king was a fact-minded man; he was not a miracle-minded man, and he lost faith in his wished-up miracle. And he said, "There must be a man. Where there is a child, there must be a man." But the Princess and the comely youth, the handsome prisoner, were a cunning pair. They still saw each other and they were not seen. Time went by and the baby became a child, and he saw no man but his father, for in secret father and son and mother met, and still they were not seen. For two years the king was puzzled, and after that time he thought up a plan. He said, "I know there is a man. I know there is a father. Of that child I know there is a father. The father has seen the child and the child has seen the father. That, I believe. If the child has seen the father he knows only one man." And he made a proclamation. To all his people he made a proclamation that all men should assemble, certain groups on certain days, and the man recognized by the child should wed the Princess and inherit the kingdom.

Do you think any man stayed at home? Only the dead ones did not come. And all were hopeful. They spent much time and went to much cost to make themselves colorful, thinking to attract the attention of the child, hoping to catch the fancy of the child. You should have seen the brightly colored robes, the brass in the ears, the brass on the arms, the ivory canes and the gold-headed canes. They tried to look attractive, they tried to be conspicuous. They were funny to see. But who could blame them? Yet the child passed them by led by the hand of the king. The child shrank from them all, day by day he shrank from them all.

One day the father fled the prison. Love found the way and the father fled the prison, and on that day he made himself present. Among the men he was handsomest, but he had no colors, he had no brass, no gold-headed cane, no ivory cane, just a crooked stick picked up on the way. And he stood aside like a humble man. The king led the child by the hand. Before the men, the hoping men, down one line and then another line, the king led the child by the hand. The child passed them by, and the child passed them by, and uttered a cry, a sudden cry, a joyful cry, and broke from the king and ran for the man with the crooked stick, the humble man with the crooked stick, the handsome man with the crooked stick, ran into

the arms of the humble man and chirped and babbled his little child-joy.

The king was glad and said, "You are the father, you are the father of this child." And the man said, "yea," the handsome, humble man said, "yea." The king set a holiday date and made a great feast and a great wedding, and he put a gold chain round the young man's neck and hung rich bright robes upon his shoulders, and he was a great prince now and heir to the kingdom. And peace and plenty went with the king to his grave, and remained with the new king to his grave, and with the king, his son, unto his grave. And they are remembered in story and song.

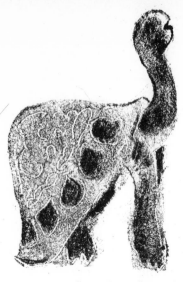

THE GREAT RACE

One time the animals decided to hold a big contest—a racing contest. The king—the lion, of course—in his unquestioned wisdom had for a long time been observing that the animals, all of them, liked nothing better than running, and prized nothing more than speed. Speed was of prime importance to animals, whether they were running from something or running to something, or whether they were just running.

For all of them, as the king in his undisputed wisdom had observed, often ran just for fun. They were not going anywhere. They were just running. And that was the best running of all. So carefree. So delightfully without destination. So purposeless. Seemingly without purpose, and yet there was a purpose. And that purpose, though not one of the animals would admit it, was to show off oneself before all the other animals, to let all others see with their own eyes just how good he was, how expert, how nimble, how swift! And each dreamed ambitiously of showing himself off so well, he could see the eyes of all others, from king to skunk, turn green from envy. Thus they leaped, ran, cavorted when they were going nowhere.

The king observed this and he proclaimed a great racing meet in which everybody was permitted to take part. Nobody was barred, and

41

the aspiring racers were numerous. And still the numbers grew, a sure forecast of a tremendously big day and a successful tournament, until the deer, the swiftest of his kind, appeared and entered his name in the race. That discouraged everybody, for the deer was known as the swiftest of animals and this one was the swiftest of all deer.

Thus nobody expected the deer, with so much reputation already established, to enter the race. They told him he should not enter, that he could add no glory to his glory, and for three days, in united action, they used every persuasive reason and force that united action can muster. But the deer went around all the time with a faint smile on his face, happily self-satisfied, and looking wiser than wise. And at the end of the three days of concerted persuasion, he announced calmly again that his name was there to stay; he *would not* withdraw from the race.

Then all the others, with their heads together, said, "What's the use?" and they began fast to withdraw. It was like a panic caused by an epidemic when everybody withdraws from an area to insure his health; and soon there was nobody intending to race except the deer, who went around still with a faint smile on his face and looking more self-pleased than ever. A good prize had been offered for the winner, and with no challenger, the deer would have the prize without even having to run for it. It was easy money. It would have been difficult for the deer to say with which he was the more pleased— with his enviable reputation or with the prospect of an easy prize. But anyway, his was a double pleasure, and he walked around all the time with that pleased smile on his face.

But the king pleaded with the animals not to let the prize go by default. Yet still nobody budged an inch. Then he roared out another proclamation to the effect that if anybody would volunteer to race the deer, the king would give a small prize to the one who came in second. He felt certain that many would now re-enter the race. But he was mistaken, for the animals are proud creatures and nobody wanted voluntarily to accept second place. That would be to acknowledge one's satisfaction with second place, and though one be actually second, or third or fourth, it is shameful to be satisfied with less than first. Satisfied, aspiration is dead, and that is a sad state of being, for one should aspire always to first place though he be lowest. And so out of pride everybody was silent and motionless, and the king frowned with disappointment.

Then finally in this tense moment, everybody heard the silence punctured by a low, squeaky voice squeaking up from the ground, and looking suddenly downwards they all beheld the turtle, the leader of his tribe, standing high on his front toes, as high as a turtle can possibly stand on his front toes, and in his squeaky voice-tones offering to race the deer for the prize. There was surprised silence for a moment, and then the animals broke loose with spontaneous uproarious laughter. They sat back on their haunches, lifted their heads and laughed to the sky, and the sound rose over the treetops and was borne for miles around.

But when they had finished and could laugh no more the tur-

43

tle was still standing there in the same position, high on his toe points. He had not cracked a smile and he looked deadly serious. And so the king set down his name and solicited more volunteers, but no others came. Then the animals waited gleefully for the day of the race. "This is the joke of the century," they said; "this is going to be good."

Meantime the turtle called his healthy tribesmen together and said to them: "Not I alone, but we together are going to win this

race. And not the second prize, but the first, for it is shameful to aspire to less than first place. Over-confidence is a fatal disease, and the deer is eaten up with that disease. I know his habits of the race. He stops and eats grass; he munches on tender leaves along the way; he stops and chats if he sees somebody he likes; and he even takes naps, and yet he has always won.

"But we must take advantage of these habits, and I'll tell you how. You know that we turtles all look so much alike nobody can tell us apart without minute examination. Now listen well. The race will be run, as you know, in the long valley between bookando[1] and boolendo[1]. I will conceal myself beneath a shrub near the end of the valley not far from the goal. And all along the way each of you will conceal himself beneath a shrub certain distances apart. One of you whom I shall name shall take his place with the deer at the starting point. Each time the deer stops to eat grass, munch leaves, chat with a passerby, or take a nap, the one of you just far enough

---

[1]Pronounced (bo o kän' do), and (bo o len' do). The words mean *upper end* and *lower end*, respectively.

ahead to see him must creep quietly out and, unperceived by him, jog stealthily onward down the valley. The one left behind will creep under the nearest shrub and lie there concealed until the race is over. Now the deer will probably take a nap this time about a mile from tne goal, thinking to dash in afterwards well rested and looking fresh as morning. And he will *know*, that I, slow-pacing Mr. Turtle, will be still far behind, and that much waiting must be endured by him and the king and spectators before I finally arrive, dusty, sore-toed and wind-broken, to receive second prize. But trust me, humble friends, I shall not keep him waiting one moment." As he ended, Mr. Turtle's solemn face for the first time broke into a smile that was somewhat like the smile of the deer, only more cunning, and the turtles danced an applause on the green, on the soft, cool green where the secret meeting was held.

On the opening day of the race every turtle was at his appointed place. Only a few spectators came to see the start-off. The great crowd had gathered around the king at the far, far end of the valley, not to see a contest but just to joke together about the great joke of the century and to have many a good laugh, for animals like to laugh and will go distances to get a good laugh. So eager are they to laugh, they often start laughing at nothing and end with thinking they have laughed at something. Thus it is easy for an ordinary wise cracker among them to pass for a real wit, and his unsuccessful wise cracks are never unsuccessful. The animals roar each time he opens his mouth. On this day everybody was ready to laugh at the ludicrous crowning of the turtle with second prize. Already their smiles were so broad they almost cracked into sound, and the smile-exposed beautiful white teeth looked like a harvest of pearls.

45

The start-off took place at sunrise with but slight incident. The few spectators who had gathered there at that early hour had to laugh when they saw the turtle start bravely jogging off, looking happy, they thought, because second prize was his—and without competition. And their laughter increased when, after two bounds which put him much ahead, the deer looked back to the turtle and bleated softly, "Goodbye-e-e," in a make-fun tone of voice. Then they all left, for the deer disappeared from view and nobody cared to watch the turtle jog slowly and tediously out of sight.

Soon the deer, grown weary, not of running, but of running without necessity, called on his nimble feet to halt the speedy nonsense and take him out to a tender green plot of grass. He had not taken breakfast before the race. He had risen only in time for the start-off, because he had slept very little since he announced himself for the race. Indeed he had had little time for sleeping because his attentions had been in great demand by the admiring does, doting and fawning constantly upon him, not one of them ever quite able to admire enough the charms of this fast, ath-

46

letic fellow. But now separated from their calling, he heard again the call of his stomach, and that tender grassy plot was the answer to his need. He took his time. He ate at leisure. Why not? He had done so before when he had had contestants in the race. Now he had none.

Meantime, the turtle who had started the race had by this time disappeared beneath a shrub as had been directed. He knew that wherever the deer stopped, a turtle up ahead would see him and glide stealthily out and away. After a long while had passed—the deer himself could never say how much time had passed — he returned to the race-way and started bounding lightly, but casually still, down the valley. He wondered if the turtle could possibly have passed while he was away, and he hoped he had done so, for then he would soon pass him up and thereby keep a check upon him, although in this race a check was scarcely necessary. "It is a boring race," he said to himself.

But about the time he said that, he spied the turtle down ahead of him, moving incredibly slowly along with his four-pace hop. He chuckled to himself and

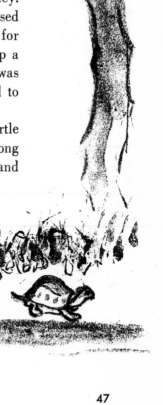

said aloud, "What a ludicrous creature! Every movement, every motion a hop. Each kick a hop: four kicks, four hops." Then he laughed again and as he passed the hopping creature he whinnied out a giggle into the sad face of the turtle, and then with a kind of kick unnecessary for the bound he knocked dust into the turtle's eyes, giggled again and disappeared from sight. Soon this turtle moved out to a nearby shrub where, with the help of another turtle concealed there, he relieved as best he could the painful smarting of his eyes by pouring into them drops of dew-water still clinging to the lower leaves of the shrub.

Next for the deer there was the munching of delicate young leaves, then the chatting with a passerby. He could not resist chatting with each one, for he seldom saw anybody because nearly everybody, as you know, was with the king at the goal-end of the valley. And each time he passed the turtle he kicked dust, just as he did with the first passing, and giggled just as before, thinking how sore and how red the turtle's eyes would be by the time he had arrived for his measly and inglorious second prize.

Finally the deer decided to take a nap while he

was far enough away, yet safely enough near the goal. But he slept longer, much longer than he had thought possible, for he had not realized how much of his strength he had given to the doting of the does. Simply expressed, he had indulged in too much night life. Had be been before the race as temperate as a turtle he could have been now as wide awake as a hoot owl. But so long he slept that the few turtles left had time to report from station to station, and the last was the station of the leader who moved out and trotted for the goal line, which, as you know, was very near, so that soon the king and spectators who were now looking intently up the green valley, expecting any moment to see the deer appear, were surprised to see the turtle instead bobbing up and down and moving with greater energy and excitement than a turtle had ever been known before to do.

But the laughter began, because everyone thought the deer had smartly decided to give them a good show, and so would encourage the simple turtle to the very end, then come dashing by only just in time to kill the poor turtle with grief. But finally the turtle drew dangerously near, and at last crossed the

49

goal line before the eyes of everybody, whereupon the king opened both lungs and let out a roar that shook the leaves of the forest, reverberated for miles around and fell like a crash of thunder upon the ears of the sleeping deer.

"Ah! Kambam bao!"[1] he exclaimed. "Was that thunder? Anyway it's time for me to overtake the turtle, unless the poke-along is still behind." And with that he bounded swiftly the rest of the way down the valley and broke into a broad grin to the spectators as he neared the goal line, pleased to think that he could dawdle so much along the way and still leave the turtle so far behind he could not even give a report of him. He crossed the goal line still grinning and

wiggle-waving his tail, only to hear and to behold the awful truth! He fainted, and was brought back by the elephant who dashed a trunkful of cold water onto him, but each time he was brought back to consciousness of lost face and lost reputation he promptly fainted again, until the elephant, tired of monotonous repetition, lifted him, body and soul, immersed him in the pool, lifted him carefully out again and supported him against a grassy bank until he could stand.

He started to faint again a few moments later when the king bestowed the prize and the medal upon the turtle. But the elephant had anticipated this weak moment and he promptly dashed another trunkful of water over him. His knees had already buckled under him but the reviving water halted the downward trend. His legs hesitated for a moment and then slowly, gradually straightened into position, but looked uncertain. This interrupted leave-taking and gradual return looked very comical, and the spectators almost split

[1]The exclamation means O God preserve me! (Ah-kämbam'bo).

with suppressed laughter, which is always more humiliating than honest, outright laughter. The poor fellow seemed scarcely conscious when the king hung upon him the badge of second prize and placed before him the insignificant money prize.

That night in the light of the moon the entire turtle tribe held a celebration dance on the broad grassy plot in the valley where the deer had fallen asleep. The deer might as well have joined them, for he, too, slept not a wink that night. And since that time the deer has been timid and self-conscious. The turtle still carries a high head.

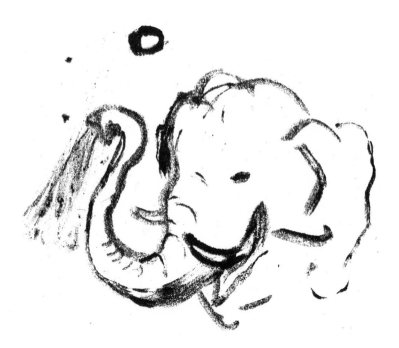

CUNNING RABBIT AND SPEEDY SPIDER

One time there was a rabbit, a very bright fellow, who was known to everybody by the name of Cunning Rabbit, and he was Speedy Spider's uncle. The rabbit and the spider are not closely related today but there are still some similarities, for both are swift of foot and ready to run at the least motion or sound, and both have the habit of raising very large families, and so both are always busy trying to solve a food problem. In famine time when food had grown scarce this problem became for Cunning Rabbit and his nephew, Speedy Spider, a hard physical struggle to provide food for their families, and worse yet, a perpetual terror to the mind.

Sometimes Speedy Spider became despondent and lay at home for hours like a man who has lost all hope. Cunning Rabbit never quit. It was not his nature to quit. He was no quitter. But then he was older than Speedy Spider. He had lived longer; he had had more experiences with hard times, and he had learned life's important lesson—that nothing bad, as well as nothing good, could last for-

ever. He knew that all things end; he had seen the end come to several famines; he had survived them and he would survive this one. He had learned that in life effort is always eventually rewarded if one only continues and never gives up.

53

And so it happened that once during his daily hopeful hopping around the country Cunning Rabbit, looking always in every direction—forward and backward, downward and upward—saw a tree on a hill beside a high wall. Of course there were trees everywhere, and Cunnning Rabbit was not in the habit of taking particular notice of trees. But he had never noticed, he had never seen, that lone tree up there before. Often he had passed this way, and he had not noticed that tree, so conspicuously alone that he wondered that he had not seen it before. Yet that wonderment alone would not have held him there staring steadily upward had it not been for the singular appearance of that tree. From where he sat the tree appeared to be bearing many white blossoms of various sizes, which is not unusual for a tree, but from each blossom there arose lazy little wisps of steam. Cunning Rabbit licked his paw and mopped his eyes for clearer vision, but still lazy wisps of steam seemed to be rising out of the white blossoms.

Then Cunning Rabbit moved across the open space and stood under the tree beside the high wall that was built around the hill.

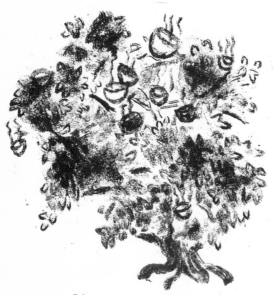

And looking upward Cunning Rabbit saw the strangest thing anybody could think of, and he wondered if he were lost and had wandered into a land filled with magic. For what had looked to be blossoms were really not blossoms. Each one was a dish filled with warm food, and lazy wisps of steam curled out from each dish. Round and round the hill by the high wall ran Cunning Rabbit like a man out of his mind and gazing all the while upward like a duck in the rain. And he swallowed often, for his mouth watered fast. Anyone seeing him would have said he was crazy from the heat or that he was drunk.

At last he himself said that such activity was stupid, and then he sat down directly under the tree and gazed longingly upward at the steaming dishes of food. At last he cried, "O, magic tree! If only you would drop down one of your dish-blossoms, just one of your small ones, O, fair magic tree! Drop it down like a blossom and tap lightly my paws." He just said that from wishing; he expected no favor, no granting of his wishes. How great his surprise when a dish tapped his forepaws. Light as a blossom it fell on his forepaws. Cunning Rabbit was startled, then he was overjoyed, but he did not fall at once with greed upon the food in the dish. He sat straight up, put his paws together, and gave thanks to the tree and all the magic powers that be. Then he ate his fill of the food, which seemed to Cunning Rabbit to be some sort of succotash, and he had enough left to carry home for his family.

The children tumbled all over him with delight after they had eaten supper, and Cunning Rabbit needed nothing more to make him happy than the gratitude of his children and a full stomach. And his happiness continued, for the magic continued. Each day he went to the hill and stood under the tree and begged

for a small dish to fall light as a blossom down onto his paws, and the tree always yielded. It never denied him.

Then one cool, rainy day Speedy Spider came to his uncle to borrow some fire, and he came while the children were eating their food, and the odor of warm food filled the room. One of the children gave a coal of fire to Speedy Spider, just as his father told him to do, but Speedy Spider did not want to leave, and to make delay he dropped the coal of fire into some water that had streamed from him onto the floor, for he was wet from the rain. "Oh!" he said. "I cannot go yet. I dropped the fire and it fell into some water." "I'll get

you more fire," said his uncle. "But wait till I'm ready to go," said Speedy Spider. "You know, dear Uncle, I perish from hunger. Give to me some strength. Let me eat at your table."

Then the uncle fed the nephew, and then each day Speedy Spider thought up some pretext for going to his uncle's at mealtime. And after eating he begged for some of the food to take to his family. At last Cunning Rabbit's wife said, "This is a great bother. Why does he not find his own food? He is younger and stronger than you are. He should go look for his food. Take him with you tomorrow and make him look for his food. Anything, just to be rid of him."

And so next day Cunning Rabbit took Speedy Spider with him, and Speedy Spider saw the magic tree and saw the magic performed. Then he too called to the tree, but he was not modest like his uncle. "I don't want a small one," he said to his uncle, and he called to the

tree, "Send down a big dish, send not down a small one. Let the biggest dish come, filled heavy with food. I will make strong my back . . ." But before he had braced himself to make strong his back, the biggest dish fell, heavy with food, and flattened the spider close to the ground.

He would have died had not his uncle been there to help him. He lifted from his nephew the big, heavy dish, but the spider was smashed and bruised and crippled, and Cunning Rabbit had much trouble to get him home. Then he had to feed him and his family until he got well, but when Speedy Spider could travel again, the tree would drop him no food, and it would drop no dish for Cunning Rabbit to give to his nephew.

But the tree dropped food to Cunning Rabbit until the famine ended, and then the dish-blossoms were no more to be seen. And

Cunning Rabbit searched for food when the famine was over, and he was rewarded, and he lived honorably with his family and kept his pride. His descendants still sit upright and look with good countenance at the world. The descendants of Speedy Spider walk close to the ground and are despised by everybody.

THE YOUNG HUNTER

He was the greatest hunter in that part of Africa, yet he wished to be surpassed in hunting skill by his young son. And so he took always the boy with him on the hunt and taught him every skill and trick of the hunt, how to know the place where the animals were, how to deflect the wild charge of the animals, how to avoid falling victim to the wild, angry animals. And he had mystic powers he imparted to his son, and he charged him to guard closely the secret, never the secret of his mystic, magic powers to impart to another.

Then one day the father sickened and died. In the time of full power the strong hunter was stricken. No medicine, no magic, no chanting, no prayers could persuade life to tarry. Life would not tarry. Death would not tarry. Life and death live always together. Death entered and life left the dwelling. Did he journey with death? Did he journey with life? Did he go to death's land? Nay, death has no land. He journeyed with death, but he went to life's land. Nay, death journeyed with him, was a guide on the way. Death guided the way, and they walked to life's land.

Then the boy bereft and the mother bereft wept hard

59

for the hunter, sorely lamented the strong man's departure. But the son remembered the teachings of the father. Already the young son surpassed seasoned hunters. Already he was the great hunter. His father had made him equal to himself, and the magic power of the father attended the son, shielded and preserved him and gave terror to the animals; they could not escape him. They could not overrun him. In herd-charge together they could not overrun him and crush him underfoot. When they thought they had crushed him, dismembered his body beneath their strong feet, he appeared out before them, farther on out before them, standing upright and laughing, defying their wrath. Then they charged him again, and again, and again, and after each charge and down-tramping of feet to mangle his body he appeared out before them standing upright, laughing his jubilance, like a god laughing down-dropped out of heaven. Then they were spent, exhausted from charging, and crush-tramping their feet where they thought lay his body. They were spent then and impotent, helpless before him, and he slew as he willed, but he did not slay all. No good hunter slays all. He did not slay all; he spared for the future. He chose well his prey, threw well the spear with direction unfailing.

Then the elephants called a council. Of all animals they suffered greatest. The youth liked the elephants best of all prey, liked best to lure them out from the forest, enjoyed most the charge of the elephants. Of animal voices he liked best their trumpeting. Unhappy was the animal liked by the hunter. Unhappy the elephants, and they called for a council. Deep in the forest they held them a council, and their trunks drooped low, so puzzled were their minds. And they said, "This is a strange hunter; we have not seen his equal. He possesses strange powers; we cannot overrun him. The secret of his magic, how can we discover? To outdo his strange magic, how can we avail?" Then spoke an old elephant, a mother of champions, lifted her trunk to show confidence in speaking, and spoke without tremor: "Magic alone can do war with magic. We must think now some magic this magic to match. One of us by magic must be made like a woman. Only a woman can worm out this secret. Man's weakness is woman. Not the hunting of elephants loves he so much. Not

the catching of great fish loves he so much. Not drinking and eating are to him so dear as is the fair woman. He is weak by the woman. A fair, scheming woman works quickly her will. We must learn us some magic. I say you no more." The elephants applauded, they lifted their trunks and trumpeted applause. But when the applause was ended they realized with trunks down that they had applauded only a plan. It had sounded good but it was yet to be effected. But the wise heads got together. They thought, they talked, and pooled  daily their knowledge and they learned some black magic. And they made a young elephant to look like a woman. It was hard work, the wise ones reported, and they praised their own work. But the whole tribe was skeptical. They asked many questions. "How could the best magic make such transformation?" "How make an elephant appear like a woman?" "How can the trunk be completely concealed?" "And the elephant bulk, how trim it down to a small maiden figure? How can magic perform it?" Then the elephant maiden was brought in before them, and at first they believed she had never been an elephant. At first they believed she had always been a maiden. Then trumpeting applause woke the forest again, confident trumpeting was borne on the wind and was heard in the villages. And the elephant-maiden was drilled with instructions, given practice, long practice, in the movements of a woman, artful and graceful. That was hardest of all for the elephant-maiden. You know that the motions of elephant and woman differ greatly, and the difference was difficult for her to master. But at last she was graceful. Then she was subtle. Then she was wily. Then she was ready!

In the village one day the heat was oppressive. The hunter was home languidly resting, not yearning for elephants, not yearning for women, just languidly resting. His chief two pleasures, woman and elephants, were far from his mind, yet he was about to get both. But he did not know that, and so he rested, languidly happy. One step into the future—it is best not to see. What Destiny deals—it is best not to know. Only the dark is preserver of joy. It is best not to know what Destiny deals. Beware of the light, beware of the light!

Who was that went by? Who was that just passed? Was that a new one that passed by his door? "I have been dreaming, languidly dreaming," he said to himself. But he went on dreaming with his eyes wide open. And he said, "I wish a new one would pass by my door. Nay, I wish a new one would stop at my door." Then imme-

diately someone darkened his door. It was not a new one. It was an old one. It was his mother. She said, "I come with a warning. Be careful of women. A new one has come. She looks subtle and wily. Be careful, be careful. She is nice to look at. Be careful of her. She has passed by this way. She prowls for a man. Be careful, be careful. I say you no more." Then he laughed and said, "Must I run from a woman, have fear of women? They have not hurt me. They can do me no harm. I like well the women." And she answered, "Women are good. Women are bad. You do not know all. You are old in the hunt, you are young in the world. Be careful, be careful. I say you no more." And she went back to her hut.

Then the son could not make ready fast enough to go walking. He would walk through the village. This way and that way, he would walk every way till he met with the new one, till he knew well the new one. He was fast making ready. Then the door became darker and a voice said, "Pardon. I am a stranger. I know not this country. I am lost in this village." He said, "You are not lost. You are with me. I am the great hunter. I never get lost. Make me your guide and you will never be lost." She let out a cry, a soft exclamation, then said, "O, of you I have heard! Your fame travels far from this land to all lands. I thought not to see you. Never to see you. How can this be? My eyes rest upon you. I thought never to see you! How can this be? I was a stranger. Now I rest in your arms. Your strong arms protect me, your strong hunter's arms. Not now am I lost. Not now am I stranger. How can this be?" Then he almost burst with man-pride. And they passed time together. Night and day were as one, and he forgot the urge of the hunt, and deep in the forests the animals enjoyed a holiday from fear. They dreaded to think of the ending of this holiday. They asked one another: "The spell of the woman, how long can it last? Her power over man, how durable is it? How soon is it broken by

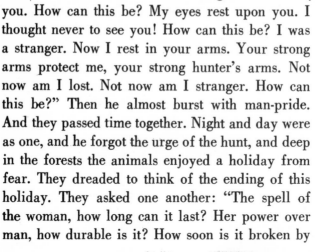

the urge of adventure far from her door? How long is this holiday?"
But that did not matter, the elephants told the other animals. Not if
the mystery of this hunter's magic could be discovered. They waited
and hoped, and hope was rewarded. For the young hunter's pride
became his undoing. He loved greatly himself and loved to hear
himself flattered, and nobody had ever praised so beautifully as this
new maiden. The more she learned about him the more could she
praise him, and her praise was sweet to his ears and eloquent with
truth. He knew it was the truth. And one night drunk on her praise
he boasted of his magic, said he had power to disappear before
charging animals. She called him god-favored, and asked where he
went to in his disappearing before the wild animals. He was drunk
on her praise, and drunk on self-praise, and he warbled his secrets
like a glad-singing bird. And she warbled her praise till he fell into
sleep, a short, restful sleep. When he awoke it was dawn. She was not
at his side. He called. She was gone. He searched.
She was gone. Then he heard loud trumpeting, loud
trumpeting nearby, at the edge of the forest the
elephants were trumpeting. Then the urge came
upon him to return to the hunt. But where was the
maiden? Where was the new one, where was the
stranger? "She will come back," he said, "while
I'm away. She will wait for me here. I will bring
her the ivory tusk of an elephant." Then he ran
for the forest-edge to meet there the elephants, and
appeared out before them laughing his confidence.
And in confidence they charged, and the charge
was ferocious, from all sides they charged, they

had him surrounded. Then the youth made invisible his body and went into a tree. But they watched for the tree that was swaying, as the maiden-elephant had told them to do, and the herd attacked the tree with great fury and broke it to the ground. Then they looked for the nearest ant hill. For he had told the lost maiden that if his tree hiding were to fail, he had still one more magic power. He could disappear under ground beneath the nearest ant-hill. The elephants could believe that, for this was a magic hunter. And so they stamped upon the place with weight and with anger. And at last they saw the mangled, mashed body of the hunter, and they went back into the forest and trumpeted three days. And all the other animals joined them with their wounds. And finally the older hunters found the mangled body of the young hunter, and they all wondered what had happened to break the spell of his magic. And his mother said it was the strange girl, the strange girl that vanished when he vanished in death. And that is why they still say

Heed well the warnings uttered by a mother.

Watch as an omen her suspicions of another.

66

THE LOVELY GIRL
AND THE LOSO [1.]

There was an African man and his wife who had a beautiful young daughter approaching the age of marriage. They were a good family but not rich. Yet in spite of being not of rich family, the girl's unusual good looks gave her a reputation that traveled distances from her home, and the worthy, reputable young men were not few who preferred her beauty to the wealth of rich girls who looked like sad disappointments to the boys after they had seen the beauty of this girl.

But the girl grew up conscious of her beauty, for she was used to hearing everyone, men and women both young and old, make strong compliments and exclamations about her surpassing beauty. So she came to have the idea that she was so very extraordinary it would be difficult to find a young man who would be a fitting match for her in marriage. She conjured up dreams of the one man, the only man, existing somewhere, nobody knew where, who alone was equal to the great honor of becoming a husband to so much rare beauty as was hers. Therefore, all the handsome men who sought her and who thought all other women suffered in comparison with her, themselves suffered disappointingly in her eyes when she compared them with her dream-man existing somewhere, nobody knew where. Thus she turned away the most eligible young men to be found anywhere—young men of the noblest blood and actually extremely handsome. She turned them away in such a condescendingly

[1] In the Vai language a loso is a horrid, legendary figure, similar to the Greek Cyclops.

67

scornful manner that a few of them, only a few, got the sickness called inferiority feeling—in relation to women—and never did recover. But most of them, after witnessing her foolish, haughty manner, rediscovered the beauty of women who had the beauty of sense.

Her father and mother were greatly distressed to see her turn away, one by one, the choicest suitors in all the land, and they reasoned with her, saying that if she continued turning away the best in the land, she would eventually be forced to accept someone inferior to her former suitors in blood, in beauty and in wealth. But she was placidly high and mighty, and she felt supremely safe, for she was living already with her dreamed-up wonder man, dwelling nobody knew where.

Now it happened that in this land, deep in the recesses of the dense jungle, the spot only guessed at and never known, there lived a dreaded loso. He had long been a sadness to this land, for he robbed and pillaged, and for food he preferred the meat of human bodies. Many a brave warrior, many a good nobleman, many a fine prince had made delicate food for the fearful, the dreadful loso in his secret lair in the dense jungle. Many years there was grieving in the kingdom for the loss of rare men to the gluttonous loso, and the king was sad and his warriors embarrassed. They had gone in war strength together hoping to slay him, but the loso was swift, wary and swift, and they never came nigh him. But against one man and against a few men the loso was powerful and glutted his appetite day after day.

Now one day as the loso secretly waited to pounce upon a caravan of travelers, he heard the whole story of the beautiful girl, and he resolved then to have her, to have her to keep. He would not devour her. Her he would keep. And he devised a way and set out for her home. And when he found an animal with the most beautiful teeth of all animals he borrowed the teeth of that animal and lent to

the animal his long out-jutting teeth. But he could keep them for only
so long. Then he found the animal with the most beautiful hair and
he borrowed hair, most beautiful hair, soft, glossy black hair, for
his head. But he had to return it. Only for so long could he keep it.
He kept on borrowing till he was the handsome somebody, the most
striking somebody, anybody ever had seen. And he came to the
home of the girl, came walking with a stately strut, and everybody
gazed with wide-open eyes. He said he was a prince from another
land but he didn't say where. He said he was a conquering man
but he didn't say what he had conquered. He said his prisoners had

served him well but he didn't say
how. But the beautiful girl was
impressed when she saw him. He
was unusual, he was different,
and he had the strangeness of being from a strange land. He
was *it!*

Her dreamed-up man was no
longer a dream. He had arrived,
and she was in a hurry to go
away with him. Her parents felt
uncertain. They begged her to
take a rare man from her own
land, any one of the many rare
men who had sought her, but

she would not hear, and she left with her dream man for his wonderful kingdom. She was proudly happy and her pride billowed up as she walked by her chosen man, the only man fit for her choosing, her dream man leading her straight to a dream land, a dream land soon to become real, as her dream man had become real.

Her handsome man made charming love in voice tones beautiful. Once he drew a kolanut[1] from his pocket, broke it in half and gave one part of it to her. "This is to make sure you do not lose me," he said. "It will help each of us to find the other. We cannot lose each other if we match halves of our kolanut." She was surprised and said, "But how can I lose you? There is nobody in the world like you!" "You are right," he said. "How right you are!" And then she laughed and said, "How clever you are!" "You are right," he said, and she laughed hard and said she loved his quick wit, and they both made the jungle ring with their laughter, for they were now walking beside a dense jungle.

Then at that moment appeared a strange animal, appeared from the jungle but at once disappeared back into the dense jungle. She saw it not clearly. He said, "Wait for me here. I will see that strange beast," and he too disappeared into the jungle. For it was the animal claiming his teeth, and the loso had no power to refuse. He had to fulfill his promise. Besides, he wished to become once more the loso, he longed to become his old self again. For only his

[1]A brown, bitter nut from an African tree. It contains much caffeine.

70

outer parts had been changed. Within he was the same, ugly as sin. He was not changed inside and so his desires had not changed. When he returned, the beautiful girl did not know him with his horrid out-jutting teeth, and when he said, "Come, let us go on," she replied, "Oh, no! Not with you. I wait for my husband." He said, "I am your husband," and he showed her his half of the kolanut. She said, "But what is the matter? What is wrong with your mouth?" He said, "It is a big joke; you will know of it later. Don't laugh yet, wait until later." Then she laughed and said, "You and your jokes! You are packed full of jokes. You are so clever!" Again he said, "How right you are!" And once more they both laughed till the jungle rang with their laughter.

Then after they had traveled quite a distance, another animal briefly appeared and at once dis-appeared into the jungle, and once more he said, "I must see that animal; wait for me here." When he returned, his beautiful hair was gone, and there was in its place only one long, ugly lock dangling from an ugly, bald scalp. She was startled and said, "You are my husband?" Then he showed her the half of the kolanut and said, "It is a huge joke. The joke is not finished. Save your laughter till later." She said, "Oh, the joke will be gruesome!" He said, "How right you are," and again that made her laugh, and she thought he must be playing an unusual joke because he was an unusual man. But for all that, she did not like to look at him now.

In this way as they traveled he shed off one by one all of his beauties, and the last to go was his

voice, which he exchanged with a fine jungle bird after they had entered the jungle and come near his dismal dwelling. Then he stood again before her and announced in his horrid loso voice that he was the loso, dreaded by her and all the people of her land, and how he had been transformed and re-transformed. She trembled and wept but she could do nothing.

He said he would never harm her but she could not go home again, and if she tried to run away she would become lost and would die. He said she would have rich clothing from caravan goods, and whatever food she desired, but as for him he would eat human flesh, and he showed her the hideous pile of human bones near the dismal dwelling. Every day he went out in the morning and came back in the nighttime bringing booty and human bodies whose flesh he devoured, sometimes uncooked, but also he made her cook for him human flesh, and that made her very sick. So day and night she lived with this hell, stirring human goulash to feed this earth-devil. And days dragged into weeks, into months, into years.

Back in her country her mother and father had no tidings of their daughter. Twin boys were born to her parents but they could send her no tidings. And the years went by and the babies became children and the children were becoming young men. But during all their growing up time they were impossible to manage. They tore up their clothes and thought it was funny to see their mother grow frantic. They broke their plates after they had eaten their food, and laughed to hear her cry and complain. Then instead of plates she used broad green leaves, but when they had eaten, they tore the food-soiled leaves into bits and littered the floor. And one day in desperation she cried, "Why do you not leave? Why do you not go away? Why not seek for your sister, your beautiful sister you never have seen? Go search for your sister. Grow up and be men. Quit bad children's ways. Become brave men, and brave a long journey! Find that far country and bring home your sister. Let me behold her, let me enjoy a long, long visit."

Then in their bosoms the folded up manhood began to unfold and they forgot bad children's ways and thought on men's ways. And they embraced their mother and spoke of their sister and said they would find that far country and find there their sister and bring her to visit. Already, they said, they knew the direction, and their mother believed them and said through her tears, "Your powers[1] have come, your strange, strange powers. No force shall withstay you, nor long can delay you. Your powers have come, your strange, strange powers. Go find that far country and bring home your sister, and greet well her husband." They swore then to do so and said, "On that day when you feel all of a sudden the west wind blow strongly upon you, know well that we come, we come with the west wind." Then she bade them farewell, and they swiftly departed.

Who can tell the heart's raptures in high aspirations? The up-swelling hope in bosoms of youth? The sense of adventure that bears youth on wings? Who can describe that? They went as on wings with a strange sense of direction. Through cool, cool forests, across burning sands, over high mountains, across rushing streams, down the long valleys, into the dense jungle they went as on wings with a strange

---

[1]The Vai believe that twins are endowed with supernatural powers.

sense of direction. To the dim, dismal dwelling in the dim, dismal jungle they came to their sister, and knew well their sister. Brothers, indeed, she said she had none. But they told of their birth, and events they related preceding their birth which their mother had told them, and now she believed them. And she wept and told of the horrid deception and her miserable life, and she pleaded for rescue. Then the boys both caught their nostrils between their two fingers and cried, "Oh, what is that odor, that foul, foul odor, what is that stench?" She said, "That stench is my husband, the stench is the loso! Oh, where shall I hide you? He is returning. He is not yet here, for his stench—it precedes him a long distance off. Here I shall hide you, up here in the bondo."[1]

And they went up into the bondo. Then soon he arrived and they heard his dread voice. "Some human is here," he cried in gruff tones. "I smell here some human. I smell human flesh." "'Tis I," said their sister, "'tis I who am human." "Not so," said the loso. "I smell a fresh human, some fresh human flesh." He began then to search while she trembled and watched, and his nostrils were true and he looked in the bondo. "How now?" cried the loso, "and what have we here?" In tears then she told him, said they were her brothers, he must harm not her brothers. Then he bade them fair welcome and invited them down, down from the bondo for good family greeting, good family mingling. But all was deceit. Inside he was laughing, inside he was gloating. They were tender, young morsels, delicate morsels. At night he would eat them. When they were asleep and their sister asleep, he then would devour them.

But there was no fear in the hearts of the boys. They had laughed heartily together while for them he was searching. Down from the bondo they came heartily laughing, making family cheer, and playing innocent of fear, said they hid to surprise him, to make his heart glad with this family surprise. He feigned happy surprise, and they feigned innocent glee. All were good actors! And without knowing

---

[1] A loft room.

it, each helped the other perform well his deceit. But the sister still trembled and stayed from them apart.

Deceit became voluble and made bedtime come late. But the loso gave them a hut close to his dwelling, made them soft beds to conduct them to sleep, deep, deep into sleep. He would fall then upon them, they would never awake, never again greet the sunrise. Inside he was laughing. These tender, young morsels—how welcome their visit! He retired to his dwelling and patiently waited, pretending to sleep. To their sister he swore that he would not harm them, they should go free of harm as she had gone free, but inside he was laughing. And when she was asleep he stole out to their hut. Deep, deep was their slumber. He opened the door. Slowly. Just a little. Cautiously he opened the door.

But a voice by the door cried up from the floor, cried into his face: "What did you say?" and the loso was startled, for the voice was strange like a voice from the dead. Which is just what it was. For the boys had brought with them the horn of a bush goat. And they placed it by the door, and they knew what would happen. A dead bush goat speaking through his dry horn can frighten a loso,

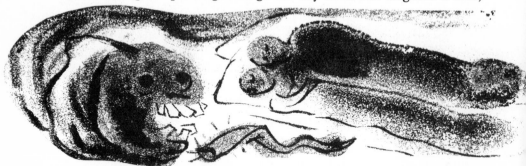

can frighten the devil. And the loso was frightened by the strange sound and went back to his dwelling. He sat there and pondered, a long time he pondered, then returned to the hut and opened the door. And the voice said: "What do you want?" The voice was here and it was not here. It was from otherwhere and yet it was here.

And the loso fled, fled to his dwelling and could not say why. What was this strangeness? Why was he frightened? Why had he run? He sat there and pondered, and he pondered till daybreak. Then the three met again, feigned family pleasure, delight in each other. "And did you sleep well?" "Yea, yea, and did you?" "O, sweet was my slumber. I moved not a finger." "And were your dreams pleasant?" "We dreamed not at all." "And heard you no sounds?" "Too deep was our slumber." "That pleases me well for my brothers to slumber, to rest from your journey, your long journey to see me."

Many more false pleasantries passed back and forth, light in their falseness, false in their lightness. Then he made his departure to stalk and to ravage, to slay and to plunder. For they said they would stay some days for their visit. He told them to be free and to have a good time, but inside he was laughing, again he was laughing, thinking of nighttime. He yet would enjoy them. He thought gladly of nighttime.

But the second night was like the first, and he thought he was sick. He had never known fear, and he thought he was sick. So he said he would wait another night. And the third day the brothers said to their sister, "This now is the day, we tarry no longer. And you shall not tarry. Make ready to come; we take you back home. We must outwit the loso and take you back home." Then she gathered some jewels taken in plunder, some jewels to enrich her, enrich her a lifetime, and they fled from the jungle and three days they journeyed.

Then they came to a river, deep-flowing river, swift-current river, and they found a canoe and were rowing across when they smelled a foul stench and heard a wild sound, and the poor sister trembled as the loso appeared in pursuit by the river. They hoped they were safe in the swift-current river, but he threw out a long hook and caught the canoe and was drawing it back to the brink

where he stood. The poor sister wept, but the brothers said, "Cease your weeping." And they drew out the horn, they pointed it toward him, and there came a weird blast, a weird blast at the loso like a sound from the dead. Then the loso was sick and sank down to the earth, he was woefully sick, sick unto death, and he died full of fear on the bank by the river, lay like a great fish dead by the river. Then swiftly they crossed the swift-current river and were glad on the shore opposite the loso.

And after two days more the mother at home looked up from her work, for she felt of a sudden strong waves of the west wind.

She quit her work, made ready to greet them, prepared them their rooms, the rooms of the brothers, the room of the daughter. The west wind was blowing and she knew they would come.

You can imagine the joyful meeting. There were laughter and tears. And the mother wept more when she heard the sad story told by her daughter. Then came the father and embraced all his children. He was proud of his sons. They had now become men. They had forgotten their little child ways. And life started anew, for they were now rich from the jewels of the loso. And the rest of his wealth they removed to their home.

Finally the twins married and made happy homes and gladdened their parents in advancing age. The daughter was wiser, sadder and wiser; her eyes were now open and she knew the full beauty of people about her. How had she not known how beautiful they were? Again she knew love, and married a good man from her own land. She came down from the elephant she never was on and discovered the beauty, and discovered the worth of men in her land. Then happiness was hers; so much happiness was hers, she made happy those about her, and from her flowed happiness to others, even after her death.

THE SPIDER AND THE FIREFLY

The spider has always been a thief and a robber and a murderer. And he is a coward, forever running, or ready to run, the moment he thinks he is detected by anybody stronger than he. But he often slays and devours those much bigger, much stronger, much braver than he by sneaking upon them and stabbing them suddenly with poisonous darts. With thieving and running, robbing and running, stabbing and running, he has developed amazing speed and surpassing agility. But one time he outsmarted himself and he got almost what he deserved. Not fully, for that would have been the death he greatly deserved, but he was so severely handled, mauled and lacerated that he received scars and alterations that have lasted him to this day and will stay with him and his tribe forever.

It happened during a famine time when food was scarce, and during that time the spider's thieving and murderous habits became more vicious than ever. That is to say, they became continuous. He was forever busy, from crack of dawn to the last ray of light, and he fretted because he could not work at night, for he was too much hampered by the dark to make good use of the night. Night is a good time for thieves, but even thieves must have a little light, just a little, to see how to steal and how to kill. The spider needed a little light in order to thieve at night, and he thought hard until he thought up a fine idea. Why had he not thought of it before? He would form a partnership with the firefly. If the firefly would provide the small amount of light needed for these dark operations, they could steal much while the world was asleep and divide the spoils. "I will have to be tactful in this proposal," said the spider, speaking to himself. "I must be as tactful as a diplomat, for the firefly has the sentiments of a gentleman. But even a gentleman can be persuaded if he is hungry enough. By this time I think the firefly is hungry enough. He has not yet been practical enough to steal during this famine, and he must be very hungry." And with that he set out to find the firefly, and found him at dusk sitting on a mangel leaf, making only a faint glow and looking very melancholy.

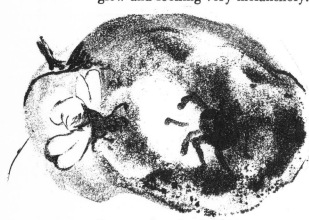

"Ah, Mr. Firefly, how do you do," called the spider in a hale-fellow-well-met tone. "I know you by your light."

"Eh, and by my light I know you," said the firefly sarcastically. And for good measure he added, "By virtue of my light I am alive. That is no doubt."

"Have I ever attacked you?" said the spider peevishly. "Have I ever taken food from your mouth?"

"No!" shrieked the firefly. "By virtue of my light, no. But— by virtue of *my light!*"

"But," said the spider seriously, "the virtue of your light will not save you from starvation in this horrid famine."

"What do you want here?" asked the firefly angrily. "If you are waiting for my light to go out in order to pounce upon me, you may as well go away. My light will shine till I draw my last breath. Then you may indeed mutilate my dead body—I would put nothing past you—but if you do I shall then know nothing of it, thank God!"

"Oh, drop your suspicions," the spider answered quickly. "Actu-

82

ally I was looking for you with peaceful purpose. I value you highly, I value your light. By virtue of your light you can be of great service to me; by my strength and agility and experience I can save your life. Listen. We can easily perish in this famine. If we only work together a little we are sure to live. I know that you are a gentleman, and I but a common thief. Yet it would be a loss to the world for a gentleman like you to die merely for the want of food, and your bright light be forever and so soon lost to bugland."

"I know, I know," said the firefly with a tremor, "and that is what distresses me. I do not care for myself. It is nothing to die. But to leave a world of bugs in darkness — the thought appalls me."

"There is no need for that," said the spider. "Not if you will lend just a little of your virtue to my vice. The reward to yourself will be the sparing of your life, but the sparing of your light to the world of bugs will be a far greater reward. It often happens that virtue must mingle with vice in order to attain the ultimate good."

"Sounds logical," said the firefly weakly. "But what is this leading to?"

"Listen," said the spider. "If I could operate at night while the world is asleep, I could get enough food for both of us. Now if you will go along and make a little light—that is all I ask, just a little light—I'll do the stealing, I'll commit all the sin, but I'll feed you to keep body and light together for the sake of the world of bugs." The spider paused, and the firefly was silent for a whole minute before he spoke.

"I was just trying to make sure," he said, "whether I hear the voice of goodness calling to duty or the voice of evil tempting to vice?"

"Judge for yourself," said the spider. "Starvation and death for yourself and darkness for bugland; food and

life for yourself and dispersion of darkness. What do you say?"

"I am doomed to life," said the firefly. "Duty calls me to life. The choice is not mine. I will go."

"Amen," said the spider. "You are a wise man as well as a good man, and that is a rare combination indeed. The good are so seldom wise. They blunder blindly in their goodness. You—you have heard the call of duty, and you have not hesitated with fear and trembling."

The firefly felt the relief that often follows decision, and he let out a fresh spurt of light.

"Cut down that light!" said the spider, nervously. "You will attract a thousand candleflies, and we will be heard and seen." The firefly switched back to dim and the spider resumed his speech. He told the firefly of a good plan he had thought of that was sure to work.

Near that place there was a stream and across this stream there was a fence. On the lower side of the fence, the leopard, another enterprising fellow, had set fish baskets containing bait much loved by fish, and each morning he took from his baskets a good catch, and thus he lived well. The watchful spider had discovered this and he was determined to have a share. But he knew the robbery would be a long, slow operation, and he was afraid to attempt it by day, lest he be caught in the act by the leopard, and he was mortally afraid of the leopard. At night by the light of the firefly turned on dim he could work with time to spare, and they would be absolutely safe. He gave further courage to the firefly by saying that if anyone should happen along, which was extremely unlikely, the firely had but to turn out his light and saunter around in the air for awhile. He himself would scamper for cover and lie there concealed until all was safe again. "You see how easy it is," he said. "I shall escape all bodily harm, and your fair reputation cannot possibly be smirched. We are absolutely safe."

And it was so, that night after night by the firefly's dim light the spider pulled the baskets to land, stung the fish to death and

extracted them one by one from the baskets, then let the baskets back
into the stream. Then by the firefly's light hovering low above him,
he dragged the fish one by one to his house where, by the time he and
his large family had feasted to their greedy content, little was left
for the firefly. This continued until the firefly grew resentful and
then angry. "I could have that much by honest effort," he said to
himself. "And if by starvation my light is to go out anyway, I prefer
to die with a clear conscience." But he was mad enough to want to
repay the spider with meanness for meanness before he died, and
he knew just how to do it.

And so the very next night after the spider had collected the fish and was ready to start dragging them home, the firefly suddenly let his light go out and without so much as a goodby, flew away. The spider at first thought that the firefly had seen or heard danger approaching and so he quickly hid himself. But after he had waited most of the night and the firefly still did not return, he decided he must drag home at least one large fish before daylight. He hurriedly pushed the dead fish into the stream, all save one big one, that they might be borne away by the current and no sign of his nocturnal stealing be left for the leopard to discover. Then he tugged at the one large fish and trusted his sense of direction to guide him home. At last after many a weary tug and pull he reached the house and opened the door. Only it was not his house, it was not his door. It was the house of the leopard. But the spider did not once guess that he had lost his way, and so he entered and deposited the fish on the floor. Then, exhausted by his labors, he sank at once into deep sleep.

It was not long till morning, and with the first crack of dawn the leopard arose, as was his habit, to go down to the stream and examine his baskets. And the moment he arose he saw the dead fish and the slumbering spider. Then he knew everything. He understood now the cause of the reduced catch for the past several days, and he knew that the thief slumbering deeply there before him had entered his house by mistake. He almost suffered from happiness, and he humorously addressed the sleeping spider: "First I'll tie you up," he said. "I'll tie you up so tightly you can't move even one of your fast-running legs. Then I'll wake you up, then I'll make a little speech, then I'll beat five devils out of you and you'll still have enough of them left with you." Then, this way and that way, he tied up the sleeping spider who slept like a drunk man, drew the cords tightly and tied the knots securely. Then after much effort he succeeded in waking the tired-out thief.

An awful tremor ran through the spider when he realized where he was and he thought to break all his previous speed records only to discover that he could not move one foot. Then he broke all records at fainting, fainting in such rapid succession the leopard had to wait a long time before he could deliver the spider the sarcastic and comical little speech he had prepared for

87

him, and which, the leopard often said later, he had enjoyed really more than the beating he administered afterwards.

But it is a great wonder that the spider survived that beating, and indeed he would have been killed had not the leopard stopped once for a short rest. He had not observed that his blows had broken or loosened the cords that bound the spider's legs, and so the scoundrel made a limping get-away and finally reached home in spite of having several legs broken, a number of feet crushed, and one eye swollen shut. But worst of all was the tight cord around the middle of his body, which had divided his body so as to resemble two hemispheres with a scarcely visible isthmus between; and his wife could not undo the knot and she could not cut the cord for fear of completing the division of the hemispheres.

Therefore it was left there to rot off, but that took so long a time that the spider's body never did right itself, and so to this day the spider looks as if severed in the middle by a tight cord. But he is still speedy and he is still a thief and a murderer. As for the firefly, he was so ashamed and repentant for this one time dimming and misuse of his light he has ever since tried to make amends by turning on all the light he has for the world of bugs. Even so, hordes of them prefer the dark. And human beings ought to know why.

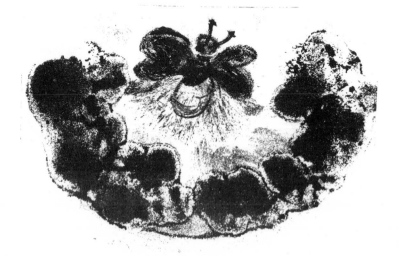

THE TWO SENTINELS

The great boa is a low sneak and a high sneak, for he robs on the ground, in the tops of the trees, and on the highest crags. At one time the eagle could not make a family because the snake robbed the nest, swallowed all the eggs, while the eagle was absent looking for food.

The eagle was the only bird feared by the boa. In fact, he feared no other creature so much as he feared the eagle. For several of his cousins, foolhardy enough to expose themselves, had been seized in the awful talons of the eagle, caught by one foot at the nape of the neck and by the other at the back's middle, and squeezed and pinched as by a vise, then borne a mile above earth and miles through the air, held all the time wriggleless. One of the cousins, only one, had survived the gruesome ordeal, but he was never able afterwards to be a high sneak.

Something happened to his vertebrae from the long, hard fall. The eagle had let him go from a great height and he struck solid rock, and would have been killed, he said, had he not struck some leafy branches some distance above the flat, solid rock, which lessened the force of the fall. That was what saved him. Even so, his injuries doomed him the rest of his life to the ground. He could never again aspire to the height of an eagle's nest. Nor did he wish to aspire to such height. Height was the one thing he had had too much of. And he told the boa: "Nothing else can be so horrid; impossible is conception of aught else so terrible as to be borne distances high above earth, held all the time wriggleless. You cannot know what it is. You have never been unable to wriggle, to make motion of some kind. I have been held wriggleless by death and tossed back into life. I bear still the nightmare. It will not leave me. Beware the eagle. You have heard me, you have seen me. Go fast from his sight, crawl wide of that bird."

The boa was impressed by these words from one who had taken the death ride and survived. He received from the account a cautious, wary fear of the eagle, so wary that he had been able to rob repeatedly the eagle's nest without getting caught. For he lay concealed in close coil near the eagle's place until he saw the eagle leave to find food. He knew the eagle did not stay away long, and so he did his work quickly, slid quickly up to the nest, swallowed greedily the eggs, then speedily hid himself safely and lay long in concealment and mute satisfaction.

Then the eagle at the next nesting time decided to hire a sentinel. There was no other hope. And so she went to the zemgbe-tutu[1] and engaged him to sit guard for an hour each day at her nest and sound an alarm if the boa came. "Help me to catch him," she said. "Just one trip to give him, one long joy-ride above the high mountains. One trip is

---

[1] A well-known African bird that makes a monotonous sound similar to doo-doo-doo-doo.

enough. Help me to catch him. Your reward will be good."

And the zemgbetutu was eager. "Just leave it to me," he said to the eagle. "Just leave it to me," he said with great courage, and the eagle left to look for food. She stayed longer this time, for she trusted the zemgbetutu, the zemgbetutu of great courage.

But when the boa appeared, hissing and grinning, the zemkbetutu lost all his courage. His voice trembled and grew weak. His alarm went nowhere. It was only a soft "Doo-doo-doo-doo." It went nowhere and the boa was not afraid. He swallowed the eggs, then hid himself again and lay quiet in well-fed satisfaction. When the eagle returned the zemgbe-tutu was still trembling, and his voice was so weak he could barely tell the awful story. "My voice failed," he said. "I don't know what happened, but my voice failed. Do you think he mesmerized me? My voice went nowhere." The eagle was angry and filled with disgust and she dismissed the zemg-betutu.

Then at the next nesting time she went to the pablo-manja[2] and offered him the job of nest sentinel. "I will try," said the pablo-manja. "I will do my best. It is not easy to face the boa, the terror of his hissing and grinning, but I think I shall not lose my courage, and I think my voice will not fail me." That modest self-confidence impressed the eagle, and she again felt hopeful of saving her eggs, but she decided not to stay away so long this time.

---

[2]A love bird. It is beautifully colored. (pab low man 'ya)

The boa was watching. The sneak coward was watching closely, and so was the pablo-manja. He would not be caught with surprise by the boa, and he turned his head round and round, as he well could do, without moving his body. He watched every direction for the quick, sudden dash of the boa. And of course, as soon as the eagle was out of sight, out into the open the boa dashed quickly, hissing and grinning, greedy for his prey. But the pablo-manja saw him the instant he came from concealment, and he set up sounds that made echoes around. He even made sounds he knew not he had. And the eagle came fast and swooped down with a loud swish of her wings and her talons were ready. But the sneak thief caught fear and ran fast away, ran far away and lay in fear for three days. Then he tried it again and many times after, but the guard was too watchful and his alarm too alarming. And the eagle hatched her eggs and raised her young. And the eagle said, "For this your reward you shall have another reward. Of all your kin, of all parrots that are, you shall have greatest beauty. In colors, none other shall match you." And since that time the pablo-manja has been the most beautiful of the parrot family because he made the most of his voice. And the zemgbetutu has ever since felt sadly inferior to other birds because he allowed fear once to make nothing of his strength.

THE BOY AND THE LION

An African despised a wife he had because she bore no children, and she herself felt ashamed before all her friends who had borne or were bearing stalwart sons and virtuous daughters. She thought, and she knew that everybody else thought, that she was being frowned upon by Heaven for something in her life, she knew not what. But for years she continued being a displeasure of Heaven, she thought, in spite of deep contrition and daily prayers, and finally the husband's disappointment turned into malice, and one day he did what she had long feared he would do.

In harsh manner he banished her to the forest, far forever from his sight. She wept sorrowfully, but she was humble and remorseful and said: "It is not seemly that I should remain all my life an embarrassment and a disappointment to you, to myself, and an object of pity to all my friends. But, sire, do not dismiss me quite yet. I do believe I have conceived. Last night I dreamed that it was true. Wait yet a little longer, and if time prove it not true, then send me forever from your sight."

Then he answered: "The same old plea you are making. Many times thus you have saved yourself, but never again. For even though time should prove your words and your dream to be true, I no longer want a child from you. You have been a cursed woman. You have long been a displeasure of Heaven. A child from you would be a cursed child. I do not want a cursed child. Go forever from my sight.

You know the penalty if you return." And sorrowfully the woman went away, far, far away, and lost herself in the deep, dark forest.

But it was true that the woman had conceived, and time proved that her words and her dream had been true. And the proof was for her both satisfaction and grief, for she knew that conception was now no redemption, no restoration. But she prayed, she struggled with doubt, and awaited her time. She found for shelter a log mammoth in size, and beneath a portion of the giant log she made a home for herself and waited for the child to wake unto life, to wake unto life with a cry and a smile. And day chased away night and night chased away day until finally the birth time came, and she had no help but bore the child alone, and when she saw she had borne a goodly son surpassingly excellent in all his parts, she wept for a long time and said, "Why, O Heaven, should so much excellence be cursed. Let not this excellence be cursed. Here is the excellence of your hands. Despise not the excellence of your hands. Let not this excellence be cursed." And she kissed the warm forehead of the babe and wept again.

Nature is often kind, and in every way it seemed to the mother that nature favored her, and the means of life she found each day. And the child grew, beautiful and strong, and each day the mother left him awhile and foraged about to gather food for herself and the child. Finally the child could walk, toddle about and play, and the mother never left him for long. She had more need to take care than she knew.

On the other side at the far end of the giant log there lived a lioness with her cub, which was also a beautiful child. And the lioness, too, each day foraged for food, but the two mothers always went different directions, each leaving her child for awhile and seeking for food, and neither had gone by chance to the other side of the log.

But one day when the mothers were away, the little boy trotted in his play to the other side of the log and beheld of a sudden the

cub and the cub beheld of a sudden the child, and somehow their hearts beat fast, with love's quick joy their hearts beat fast and friendship ripened in a moment's space. It was a beautiful thing to see, and the birds beheld it and made a symphony of their throats, for birds know best the heart's glad ecstacies. And now each day the child and the cub freed the heart of the other of loneliness, and the tree-top symphonies played on, as the child and the cub passed joyous, playful time together and developed a language intelligible b e t w e e n them. And instinct told them when to part. Whichever one visited the other, instinct told them when to part, and so the mothers never knew.

Now it happened one day that in their pursuit of food, the woman and the lioness met in the forest, and the lioness sprang upon the woman and crushed her with one blow. Then she dragged the woman near to her lair and left her for later eating. But the cub knew nothing of this.

At home the child waited for his mother, but his mother did not come. He felt a strange fear, and he did not know what the strange feeling was, for he had not known fear before. Night and darkness without his mother—that was new and strange and unpleasant. But at last fear surrendered to sleep, and he awoke with the sun, feeling

95

hopeful now that his mother would come. But as time passed she did not come, and he felt troubled again, and when he knew the visiting time had come he went quickly to the cub and poured out his anxiety in the language common to them.

Then the cub felt a suspicious fear and said, "Let us search for your mother. Come, let us search." And they had not searched far before they found the mangled body of the woman, and the child wept piteously over the body of his mother. Then the cub said, "My mother has done this. And soon she will find you, and then I will have no friend as you have no mother. Your mother has died. My mother must die, else you will die, and I cannot let you die. I do not belong to my kind. I have not a lion's heart. How is this I have not a lion's heart? How is this I have a human heart? How have I your heart, and know your heart and you know mine?"

Then the two wept together, and afterwards the cub told the child how his mother must come to death. And it came to pass, indeed, that when the lioness was deep in exhausted sleep they plunged into her heart a great knife that had belonged to the boy's mother. Then in sorrow they made graves and buried the two. Afterwards

the cub moved over to the child's shelter, and the two lived together, and together they grew to maturity.

Then one day the lion said, "You are now a man. You must not forever stay away from your kind. And you will marry and make you a home." The boy answered, "Yes, that I will do. But I will not always be separated from you. I must meet somehow with you. Our hearts are knit together. Death alone can unravel them. We cannot remain always apart."

"No, indeed no," said the lion. "I shall visit you. When you are alone, I shall come unseen to you."

Then the boy left the forest and went to the world of men. And though he knew it not and they knew it not, he was in the town of his father. And everyone was saying, "Have you seen the handsome stranger, have you seen that beauteous youth?" And each would answer, "Yea, yea. From whence has come this beauteous youth? O, that my daughter might have that handsome stranger!" And everybody, including his father's house and all the kinsmen, feted and entertained the comely youth, but none knew, as indeed he knew not, just who he was.

Finally he made happy an eminent man by taking his daughter to wife, which grieved every other father in the town, including his own father who, ignorant, of course, of the youth's identity, desired his own son for a son-in-law. And the youth established a good home and he prospered well and his bride was happy.

But eventually a cloud gathered over her happiness, for there were times when her husband insisted on being alone—absolutely alone. There could be no intrusion. There were times, he said, when he must have isolation absolute, uninterrupted. His commands were adamant, and at those times he seemed detached from the whole wide world of men, and sat at night in his room alone without a light. What was he doing? Was he in deep meditation? Was he involved in matters clandestine and afoul of tribal tradition? Or was it another woman, or women, that engaged him? The more the young wife wondered, the more uncontrollable grew her curiosity and the wilder her jealous fear.

At last her mind was made up, and one night she crept to the door and listened. She could hear nothing distinctly, but indistinctly there were strange sounds, sounds like conversation that were not like conversation—not like conversation she had ever heard. But he was not alone; and jealousy, piled suddenly onto jealousy, drove her insane and she suddenly threw open the door to behold in the moonlight her husband and a majestic but dreadful lion sitting close together and engaged, it seemed to her, in low and intimate conversation.

She screamed a terrible scream, and the neighbors ran quickly with guns and spears, and any other weapons they could quickly seize. The lion dashed out the door but many shots ran after him and he was mortally wounded, but limped painfully all the way to the forest home. The youth would not explain to the curious townsfolk. He sank into silence and would not talk, and they thought him

99

sick from fear. Secretly, he hoped his friend had escaped untouched. He knew he was swift and he believed he was safe.

But the next day sorrowfully he traced him home by the telltale blood, and over the body of the lion near their forest home he wept out his grief. Then he made a grave, placed within it the body of his friend, and then there in the grave he plunged into his own heart the same knife that had taken the life of the lioness. There the townsfolk found them. After much wondering and guessing and never-knowing, they left them together and covered the grave. Today the people there still tell the story, and guess and wonder.

THE TRIBES
THAT UNITED

Once there were two tribes in Africa that had long felt enmity for each other, and this enmity had several times broken out into open conflict. Everybody had forgotten the original cause of the enmity, but neither tribe, it seemed, could forget the enmity itself. It happened that at one time each tribe had for leader a young man, each of them already renowned as a warrior and a sagacious leader. And each leader felt genuine respect for the other because their great qualities were quite alike. But because of the traditional tribal enmity, they respected each other from a distance, and yet this mutual respect preserved peace between them for a long time. And peace might have continued until the two tribes had grown into a common understanding and permanent peace had it not been for an affair of the heart.

It seems a strange thing that love slays peace and understanding. But love has always been the source of conflict. Maybe not love of the right thing, but too much love of something has always started war. And so it happened that one day the leader of one tribe was strolling by the border-land between the two tribes when a beautiful girl of the other tribe was strolling there with some of her friends. She was famous in her tribe for her beauty, and her own king had it in mind to marry her but he was waiting until she became a little older. In love, procrastination is fatal.

The foreign prince spoke to the girl and wooed and won her heart then and there. He was a greater gallant than the other prince, and the beautiful girl felt limp from desire for the gallant prince. What mattered it that he was a foreigner? What mattered it that he was the leader of the other tribe? The heart in love forgets all else. She helped the prince to steal her. She helped him to kidnap her, and she made it look to her friends that she had been seized and carried away. Yet the affair did not cause war, for the other prince preferred not to care, or to seem not to care.

Otherwise, it would appear as a loss of face, and he thought he would look ridiculous, and he was too proud, and truly he was too high, to permit that. And so he waited and hoped for a logical pretext, or a seemingly logical pretext, to humble his daring neighbor. But that did not come for several years.

In the meantime the other prince and his stolen bride had had happiness added to happiness by the birth of two beautiful daughters who were now growing into young womanhood, and their beauty was known and talked of throughout their tribe, and they were loved as were their mother and father. Who could believe that so much happiness and peace and perfect living could be quickly changed for grief? Not the beautiful child-daughters.

Yet it happened one day that a border fight occurred between warriors of the two tribes, and many men lay dead in the sun. Then the prince who had waited for a pretext of war said, "This is the time!" And without warning he swept across much land in the dark night with his warriors and fell upon the capital town of the rival prince with great and sudden slaughter and burned the town. The prince was slain defending his people, and the wife and mother perished in the slaughter, but not before she had helped her daughters to escape to the forest. There they sheltered themselves and lived apart from the world for many months.

Then one day one of the girls walked alone by the forest border of the rival tribe but of course she did not know where she was. And she did not know she was fated to be separated from her sister, to lose her sister almost for a lifetime. For she met by the border with young men and young women strolling leisurely, and happy in merriment. And they talked with her and were pleased with her and drew her into their company and would not suffer her to depart. They knew she was not of their tribe and they were entranced, for the foreign is strangely alluring, and they prevailed upon her to be of their company awhile, and she strolled with them back into their town.

The prince saw her and was smitten with her, but he did not know she was the daughter of the prince he had slain, and she did not know he was the prince who had warred on her tribe. He would not let her depart and he made a young bride of the beautiful girl, and soon a son was born, a comely child, surpassingly fair. But now she was resented and despised throughout the tribe. Why had the leader taken a bride from another tribe? She was a stranger and an unknown. She was all right as a stranger among them, dwelling among them as a lost stranger, but not as a bride of the leader. Why had he done this? Now he was a slave to the charms of the beautiful foreigner, and the people shook their heads and talked low together. She was a witch, they said, a beautiful witch, and the king was bewitched, he was slave to her charms and he loved that child more than he loved all his other children. Would that child some day be made their leader, the ruling prince of their tribe? They shuddered and made intrigue together and plotted to poison the child.

Then the mother pleaded with the king to let her hide the child away in the land of another tribe. Finally the king, distressed because of his people's displeasure, reluctantly gave his consent. Then the king and his wife went away on a journey, and unknown to his people they entered the land of a poor neighboring tribe. But into that tribe they went as plain persons, and the people knew not that greatness and power walked among them disguised. And in that land they talked often with a slave and his wife. And the king in disguise purchased the freedom of the slaves, gave back to them their own lives and made to overflow with joy their hearts. But he bound them to silence then, and told them the desire of himself and his wife. "You are to take our child," he said. "You will be mother, you will be father to this child, and he shall be as your son."

Then he revealed to them his identity, and the ransomed slaves were awed, and they kissed his hands. Then he said that if they kept not the secret, their freedom would be lost, and they swore the secret would go with them through life into death. Then he had made for them a home and made to them gifts for a good life to the day of their dying, and for the full growth of their son. Then with tears and embracings they left the beautiful child and returned to their land. At home the king told how their child, the beloved, the beauteous child, had sickened and died on the journey. And the people were glad and secretly together rejoiced, and when they saw the tears of the mother they still could not be sad.

Now when twenty years had passed the king was weakening with age. As he walked with the days toward death his mind became more and more troubled for the future of his tribe. Would they find a wise leader? Would they choose a weak leader? For the future of his tribe his mind was troubled, and he called for the magic seer, the teller of things to come, and commanded: "Tell me, O Teller, tell me of things to come. Peer into times unborn and tell me of things to come. Blessings or evil therein, show me the things to come.

Tear apart the dark curtain and show me what is to come. And show me the leader to come."

Then the magic teller went into long isolation and came back to the king and said: "Not good, O Leader, is the pregnant future. Not good, O Leader, is the future to see. The chief of another tribe will take over this kingdom. Send me no more to look at the future."

Then the king was sorrowful and he wept. How had he won the displeasure of Heaven? What sin of his doomed his tribe to be thrall to another? He cast his eyes back over the past, and he shuddered each time he remembered the vengeful slaughtering of the rival chief and his city. "That was my sin," he said, and he prayed and repented. He begged of Heaven, but the magic teller saw always the same thing. But when his wife heard him speak for the first time of the long-ago warfare, she knew she had wed the respected rival of her father. But she locked her surprise within her, and sorrowfully watched the declining king with tender care.

Then finally the king died, and the vengeful, willful men of the kingdom created them a leader who was a weak leader, and that is the reason they made him the leader. They wished themselves to be the power, and so they made a weak leader. A weak leader is never the leader. The selfish love a weak leader. With a weak leader they have a big day. They have a big day, but not so the people. Then the right men must act for the sake of the people. The right men must act and make safe the kingdom. And when they saw the kingdom grow weaker and weaker, the right men arose. They were lovers of right, they loved first their land, not themselves first, and they removed the weak leader and banished his friends.

Then they looked for a leader and they called a wise leader, the wise young leader of a weak tribe to come be their leader, to take the great throne of a great tribe. He was wise and had wrought greatly for his weak tribe, and his fame had crossed borders. He united the two tribes, and in the capital town of the strong tribe he mounted the throne, the united throne, and the people, united, shouted applause with music and song. They did not know he was the son of their former king, their warrior king who had died. They did not know and he did not know. He was the son of former slaves. Of that he was proud, and of that they were proud, for tribesmen like a man so strong he can rise from the lowest to the top place of his tribe. And they knew he was the child of destiny, too. He was the will of Heaven, they said, for had not the magic teller foretold what now had occurred? The leader of another tribe had become leader of their tribe, but by peaceful consent he had come, not by conquering war.

Then one day the mother and father stood up in the court. They that were once slaves spoke to the court and spoke before the king. "Hear us," they said. "Hear and believe. This son is not our son. This is the son of your great king, and his mother lives quietly among you still." Then they told the whole story as you have heard it already, and they brought other proof, brought unfailing proof which the king long ago had left in their keeping. And the people were astonished, as the king was astonished, but the people were glad. They said their king had returned, had returned in this son. They loved now his mother, and they restored her to

107

favor and to honor at Court, and the foster parents they did not forget.

Then came another happy surprise, for the long-lost sister who had long ago rejoined her tribe heard all this strange story and knew then that this king's mother was her sister. There was a glad meeting when she came to this Court to see there her sister, herslf the aunt of this great king.

And so greatness came back to the Court and the kingdom, and the people were happy again. And when the rival tribe saw that their slain king's daughter had been married to her father's rival, and that she was mother of that tribe's king, they called him to be their tribal leader, too. Then the old enmity vanished, and a new, great kingdom was established in Africa, and peace, not war, prevailed.

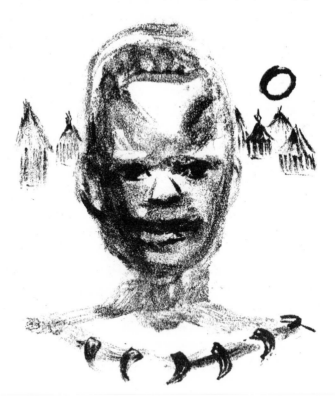

THE BANISHED MOTHER

There was an African who had one barren wife and a younger wife who was fruitful and had borne him two sons. And he loved well both wives, the barren and the fruitful. He did not despise the barren wife because she was barren, as many Africans often do. To each he gave love alike and favors and honor.

But the barren wife felt jealous of the other. She could not help being jealous. Greater love, she said to herself, would go at length to the other. Greater favor the other would draw. How would it feel to be quite forgotten? How would it feel to be quite forsaken? To be possessed and know no possessions, how would it feel? And she thought the pain of the fear must be nothing to the pain of the fact. She did not know that fear is more terrible than fact. And so her fears watered and tended the green plant of jealousy, and the roots went deep in her soul and the leaves covered over her heart.

And jealousy gave birth to plots and she thought of a way somehow to turn to disfavor the favor of the young, fruitful wife. But she concealed carefully her feelings, and the young wife did not know of these feelings seething in the heart of the other. The young wife loved well the other and often had said to the other: "My children will be children to you, my sons will be sons to you, and not one mother but two they will have. It was you who helped with their borning, stood by me with help at their birthing. Sons to us both they shall be and the love of two mothers be theirs." And the other feigned humble manner and said, "Yea," but she thought of ways. She had been mid-wife before to the other, had eased for the other the birth throes, but now she thought upon ways, and hopefully bided her time.

Then again the young wife conceived, and when at last the time had come, she begged of the other to stand by her, to aid her again in the borning, to ease her again the birth throes. Then the barren wife stood by, bound her eyes as before with the bandage[1], eased for her the pangs that racked her, and said to her comforting words. And twin sons were delivered, wondrous of beauty in face and form. But the jealous woman brought the two halves of a calabash[2] and placed the children together in one part of the divided kongo and set the shell afloat on the river. And she got two newly born puppies, squirming, and sticky from birth. Then she said to the mother, "I fear to unbind now your eyes. Oh, that you might look elsewhere forever! I fear for the shock to your eyes. Oh, that you might look elsewhere forever and see not what you have borne. Oh, that you might never behold what on this day you have borne!"

---

[1] It is the custom to bind the eyes of the expectant mother. The idea is that preventing the mother from observing the birth spares her nervous excitement.

[2] A large gourd.

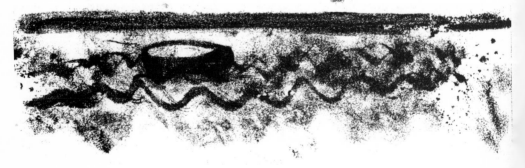

And the blinded woman, weak and trembling, said, "What deformity has Heaven decreed; what deformity bears my offspring? What is the measure of this affliction? Unbind now my eyes and reveal to me this affliction."

Then the other wife said, "Wait. Wait till I bring our husband to stand by your side when you see this." And she went to the husband and said, "Gather your strength, a curse is upon us. By my dear fruitful sister, a curse is upon us. Heaven's displeasure has come to my sister, the curse, it is horrid! Gather your strength, I am weak from this horror."

Then she told the husband what had happened and he went himself to see and beheld the sticky, whimpering puppies in the other half of the kongo shell where she had placed them. And he thought they sounded like children, and that made them more horrid. Then he said, "She is cursed now of Heaven. Something she has done and Heaven is angry. There is no help for her now; a curse is upon her. She must go her own way, for a curse is upon her, and Heaven will smite us if she go not from us." Then he set the puppies afloat on the stream and looked not toward them again.

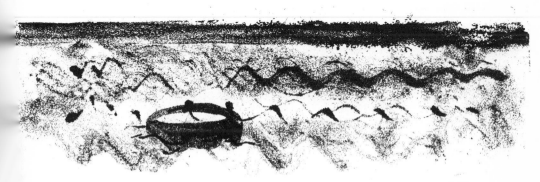

And when the young woman was again strong he told her sadly of the curse that Heaven had sent, and how she must go far away with her curse. And she wept and said, "I must take from your house Heaven's displeasure. Lest curse come to you and our sons I must bear far this curse. I must not give Heaven's displeasure to you and my sons." And she embraced him and her sons, then turned her back and departed. And the barren wife wore three days a sad face, but within she exulted.

Now far down the stream there lived a poor fisherman and his wife. And when the fisherman saw the kongo shell floating downstream, he rowed out to it and lifted it into his canoe, astonished to find two excellent babes, surpassingly excellent babes, and the man and his wife rejoiced. They had yearned all their lives for a child. Now Heaven had sent them a gift, on the current of the stream this double rich gift Heaven had sent them. How tenderly they tended the babes. Then down on the current came another half of a kongo shell, and in wonder he beheld it and rowed out to meet it. Then in faith and in wonder he beheld the puppies and he said to his wife, "Heaven is pleased and smiles on the babes; down on the current Heaven sends gifts, companions for the babes."

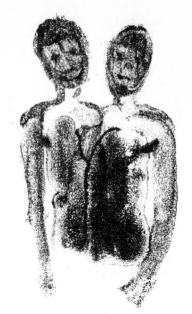

Then the years passed on and the twins grew into lads beautiful and swift and strong, and they exceeded in excellence all others around them. And it happened one day that the father stopped there on a journey, rowing down the long river, and he craved to pass the night there; and the elderly pair said, "Yes, pass the night here. Be a stranger no more and pass the night here."

Then they looked at him hard, then gazed at their sons and looked at each other and back at the stranger. And they said, "This is a strange wonder; our sons look just like you. This is a rare wonder."

Then said the stranger, "This is a rare wonder, indeed a rare wonder. These lads are two pictures, like my image in water. Whence got you these lads? You are too old for these lads. Whence got you these lads?"

Then they told the strange story of the Heaven-sent kongo shells borne on the stream, first the shell with the babes, then the shell with the pups; and the man was aroused and made careful questions. And

the time of these gifts to the elderly pair was the time of the labor of the wife he had banished. And the shells were there, preserved by the elderly pair, and the parts fit together. Then he said to them, "There shall come more reward yet, greater gifts shall come to you. Wait for my return." And he went back up the stream and rowed out of their sight. And the old ones said, "Is this Heaven's bright messenger looking after these gifts? Pray we have done well and that Heaven is pleased." And they waited and hoped.

Then after some days the stranger returned, and with him the wife. And he said, "Let us stop here. Let us visit this elderly couple." And again there were the lads, and two dogs were their playmates. And he said, "Look at these lads, like my image in water. They were borne on the current in a kongo shell and the fisherman found them. And these dogs are the puppies I set float on the stream in the half part of a kongo. Look at the parts of these shells; they belong to each other. All came from my house, and is this not strange?" Then she fainted from guilt; she could not hide her guilt, and she pleaded for mercy. But he banished her forever, and he took home his children to live with their brothers; and the elderly pair he took back to his home and kept them till death. And he found the poor banished mother and prayed her forgiveness and took her back home. Then his long sadness left him, and happiness came there and dwelt there unbroken.

THE PRINCESS TURNED SERVANT

She had been secluded from the world by her father. You see, sometimes an African chief or king decides to bring up his baby daughter princess completely away from the company of boys, away from the presence of rowdy, determined young men so that he can be sure she will grow up refined with womanly grace, and certain to remain a virgin, chaste unto the day she is given in marriage. But this princess grew up so very detached from life in the world outside her enclosure that she was completely ignorant of the kind of world she lived in and the kinds of people that fill this world. Of mountains and valleys and oceans and rivers she was ignorant. That people were good and bad and indifferent she did not know. For her father had tried hard to make her innocent, so hard he had made her mainly ignorant. And innocence that comes out of ignorance is not the best innocence. Real innocence comes out of light, comes out of knowledge, comes out of truth. Innocence that comes out of ignorance leaves one weak in the world and puts him in danger. You know how it is with a bird, like a canary, that has lived all its days in a cage. If you set him suddenly free in the world, how long will he last? How long?

But the king, her father, did not know all this. He was more good than wise, which is not the best good, but that is the way he was. And so he tried to make his daughter innocent, tried to keep her chaste by separating her from life. It happened that she was good,

115

her heart was naturally turned toward loving-kindness and right-doing. Because she happened to be naturally good she never would have needed this kind of seclusion, but her father being more good than wise didn't know that, and so he made his daughter innocent and ignorant and weak. God, forgive him. Yes, God, forgive him.

But let's go on with the story.

The young princess was schooled and trained in all the rituals and ceremonies of the tribe. Then at last she was a young woman and she was made ready for marriage. And the chief of another tribe heard of her and wanted her for his oldest son who would inherit his throne. So he called to him some trusted taindu-nu[1] and said: "You know that all men born are born to die, the known and the unknown, the strong and the weak, the wise and the foolish, all come into life alike, and in death again they are all the same. I too must go, and I know not when. But I have my son, the Prince, who will take my place. Yet he too must die, and as yet he is not wed; no son has he to take his place. He has spoken to me for the daughter of a great chief I know. Her father has kept her secluded. She is a spotless virgin. My son, the Prince, desires her. Bear to the chief her father these gifts from my hands and this message from my lips and from the heart of my son, and bring me back the king's reply."

The taindu-nu said, "It shall be so," and they bowed low and departed.

And in his capital town the king received the taindu-nu and did them honor. And he was pleased, for he had heard at other times proud reports of that stalwart prince, and he knew the worth of his kingdom, though their kingdoms were a distance apart. Thus he was happy to give his daughter to a worthy prince,

[1]Emissaries. The word is from the Vai language.

116

happy in the thought that his daughter's husband would become a king, happy in the thought that his daughter's son would become a king. Down through the future he counted kings. Down the dim ages kings walked forth and walked out of sight down the dim ages, and other kings f o l l o w e d ; through his son in his kingdom, through his daughter in the other kingdom he saw kings walking forth bearing his blood down the long, long ages. He could see kings. He counted crowns,  and lost count in the dimness of the dim ages. And for three days he made feasts to the visiting taindu-nu and at last they departed, bearing return gifts to their king and the prince.

By and by the time came for the king to send his daughter, as he had agreed to do, to the tribal prince in his capital town, a long journey away. But he would send no men, no guards with his daughter. He was going to keep her still only in the company of women, until she was joined with the prince in his own city. And he sent her away quietly in company of one of her waiting women. She had long been with the princess, and the princess loved her and the king trusted her with great confidence. He gave a king's blessing with admonitions to his daughter and a king's instructions to the servant woman. Then they left him and soon became shadows in the distance, and at last his eyes could behold them no more.

Now for the first time the princess was seeing the world, seeing it as a little child beholds each new thing as a miracle—as everything really is. Like a little child the princess was seeing the world. And she exclaimed and babbled and bubbled over every little aspect of nature, over every little beauty that nature produced. And everything made a question in her mind and dropped the question off her lips. The servant woman very soon became bored from answering simple questions about simple things, and an idea came into her mind, a wicked idea, for actually she was a cunning, crafty woman. She was not good in heart as the king believed. She was a crafty fox. So when they came to a babbling brook of clear water the princess again out of puzzled amazement made a question: "What, oh what is it?" she cried. "Whence comes so much water? I never knew so much water, and all in one place? Whence comes this water? Where is it going? Why is it going? How is it going? What makes it its hurry? Why is it so happy? What is it singing? Oh, tell me the story, the story of this water!"

Then said the servant woman: "This is a great mystery. This is a dark secret that cannot be told, not without price. Without price there would be penalty. We would be stricken with sores. It cannot be told without price. With price we are spared."

And the princess said, "I perish to know the story of this water. Tell me the price. I must know the story of this water."

Then the servant woman said, "It is a heavy price and I do not like it. But in no other way can we avoid the penalty. You must

take off your fine sandals, the sandals of a princess and exchange them for these, the sandals of a servant."

The princess said, "That will be easy. Take off your sandals." And they exchanged sandals.

Then they were funny to see: a servant woman wearing royal sandals that did not accord with the rest of her dress; a princess in royal dress that did not accord with the crude sandals on her feet. Then they sat down by the cool, babbling brook and the princess heard eagerly the story of water. All about water she heard, and she learned with surprise about rivers, many, many times larger than the brook, rivers with people in boats rowing up and down them. She learned about lakes that mirror the sky, and of great seas and the measureless oceans. Her imagination took wings and bore her away over the measureless oceans, around the shores of the world and back to the glad-singing brook, to the cool resting place by the glad-singing brook. And she was happy with her new-found knowledge, and she traveled on until they came to a very large tree. She had never seen a tree so large. She did not know any plant in the world grew so large.

"Oh, what can this be?" she cried with wonder. "And how can this be? Pray how can this be? I knew never a plant could grow so large and so near to the sky. Say, what is it called? Tell me the story, Oh, tell me the story of this great giant plant."

The servant woman said, "There is a price for the story, else the penalty will be grievous. Yet the price is too great and I do not like it."

119

Then the princess said, "Tell me the price. I must know the story. I thirst for the story. I perish from thirst."

And the servant woman said, "You must take off your royal headdress and exchange it for mine. The price is too great. I do not like it, but the penalty is worse. Let go the story. The price is too great."

The princess said, "Take off your headdress," and they made the exchange.

Then they were funnier than before to look at: head and foot were now in accord, but garments between fought headdress and footdress. But they sat down in the cool shade of the great tree, and the princess heard all about trees, the pines of the north, the palms of the tropics, the beeches, the firs, and the fruit-bearing trees. And she was happy with the knowledge, and thought the price nothing for all she had heard, and she yearned to learn more. Then they traveled until they came to a pool of water where were some beautiful white swans gliding gracefully at leisure upon the clear water, and the princess went into ecstacies. "Oh, tell me what these creatures are, these beautiful creatures," she cried, clasping her hands in adoration. "Oh, beauty, floating on beauty! Oh, beauty, mirrored in beauty. Oh, beauty, enveloped by beauty below, above and around. Oh, creatures of beauty in beauty, I must know your story!"

"Forget their story," said the servant woman. "You know the penalty without price and the price is far too great."

"I command you to tell me the price," said the princess, and

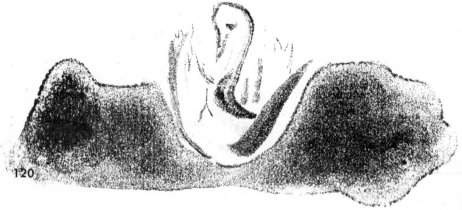

the servant woman said as if in distress, "You must give to me your royal dress and the other garments, and you must put on this common servant's dress. But forget, forget those birds!" She buried her face in her hands as if in distress, but she knew what the princess would say.

The princess commanded her to take off her servant's garb, and they made the exchange. Then except for the royal jewels that adorned the princess, the princess looked like the servant and the servant looked to be the princess. And it was funny to see a person garbed like a plain servant and wearing royal jewels. But just at that moment a serpent beautifully colored slithered across the grass by the pool, and the princess gave her jewels for the story of serpents. Then she looked completely as a servant and the servant as a princess. But the greatest bargain was yet to come.

Somewhere on the journey there came a little rain shower, and after the shower a great rainbow. Now the princess had seen bits of the rainbow from her enclosure, but never the whole rainbow. Now she was enthralled with so much mystery and beauty, and she made exclamations. "What is this great mystery, this miracle of beauty, profusion of beauty striding the world? Where is the ending, where is the beginning, how long is the lasting? Where goes it in hiding when no more we behold it? Tell me about that land, for there will I journey and dwell there forever!"

The servant said, "The price is much too much. You would have to keep secret at the court of the prince that you are the princess.

You would have to play my role as servant and appoint me to play your role as the princess. But you would go on learning the secrets of great mysteries. Every day you could secretly command me to tell and I would have to tell. But neither of us could ever reveal the secret that you are the real princess, for then we would be smitten with sores, horrible sores. And the prince and the king, his father, and the queen, his mother, would likewise be eaten with sores, as would the king, your father, and the queen, your mother. Horrible would be the death, but death would be sweeter than life."

And the princess said, "Learning and knowing is the best thing my life has yet found. I think I had no life until I started learning and knowing on this journey. I will not turn back from learning and knowing. I will keep the secret. Knowledge is best. Princess or servant, knowledge is best." And from that moment on she served the servant turned princess, and the servant lorded the princess turned servant.

Now when they came to the capital town of the prince, great honors were done the arrival of the princess, but you know how the wrong one was honored. And the great wedding day came with many festivities and great rejoicings, and the prince, the worthy prince, married the common servant. A princess and a spotless virgin he thought he had wed, but she was no princess! It was not long before the court loved and marveled at the beauty and goodness of the servant girl, who was the real princess. But nobody knew and nobody suspected that she was the real princess. And she was happy each day in some new-found knowledge, and day gave chase to day and knowledge was added to knowledge. Then at times she suspected the honesty of the servant woman, now princess, but she feared the curse of sores might prove true. So days gave way to weeks, weeks to months, months to years. And two years passed by.

Then one day the king, her father, spoke of his daughter. In his court, before princes and servants he spoke of his daughter. "How

is it," he said, "with my daughter? I wonder how it is with my daughter and the great prince, her husband. I will journey to that court. I will gladden my daughter and the prince, and make glad mine own heart by gladdening mine eyes. I will see my daughter." And he journeyed to that court with a company of worthies and with servants, and he bore rich gifts to the king and to the prince and to his daughter. When he arrived at that distant court he was received with the joy of glad surprise, and the greatest royal honors were accorded him. Then he said to the prince, "And how is my daughter? How find you my daughter?"

"Well," said the prince. "She soon will appear herself here to greet you. Messengers have gone bearing announcement."

But a long time passed and still the princess did not appear. For the servant woman turned princess was walking her chambers and shaking with fear. She knew not what to do. Guilt trembles in darkness but grows sick in the light. She was trembling and sick. She could not stay, she could not go. And time passed. Then said the prince, "The princess prepares over-much to do you great honor. Let us rise and go meet her, or find her at home being decked by her maidens in array best to greet you." Then they went there, the king's heart high in anticipation. And the servant woman turned princess stood at last, pale and trembling, before him. The king stared empuzzled while the prince wondered at this strange behavior of father and daughter. Were they numb with delight at seeing each other? Why trembled she so? Why stared he so strangely?

At last the father turned to the prince. "Where is my daughter?" he asked in accents slow and deliberate, more like a demand than request. "Where is my daughter?" he said.

"Here," said the prince, "here is your daughter."

"Nay, nay," said the king. "Tell me, where is the one who came with this woman?" For underneath all the royal adornments the king discerned his servant, the crafty, false servant he had thought was so faithful. His demand he repeated and the prince answered, "The servant? The beautiful servant girl the princess bore with her? She is with the servants. She is in the servant quarters."

"Send for her," said the king, and he was obeyed. but the prince knew not what to think.

And then the real princess appeared, lovely in humility, royal in rags. She ran with a cry, a glad cry when she beheld of a sudden her father, and he took her in his arms and embraced her and kissed her while others looked on with wonder and the false woman trembled, sick with her guilt. He pointed a finger, a long finger he pointed,

125

and she felt it a sword piercing her heart, her sick, false heart pierced by his finger. "That," said the king, "is my plain servant woman, my false servant woman. This is my daughter, this is the princess. How has this happened? Who made this deception, who hatched the foul deed?" And the daughter told all, told the whole story as you have heard it before, and the king was wroth and the prince was furious. Then the false servant fell down on her knees and begged them their mercy. But she was thrown to wild beasts, to hungry, wild beasts that mangled and devoured her, and she soon was forgotten.

The princess, lovely in rags, was resplendent in royal array. Yet she added more to dress than dress added to her. And now she was wise in innocence, not ignorant in innocence, and beautiful in prudence. And she added to the wisdom of the prince, and when finally he went to the throne she was a queenly helpmate at his side, adding womanly dignity and honor to the peace and plenty of their long, long reign. In death they sleep side by side. And her sons and sons' sons walk royally still down the long ages. But down the dim ages the world has lost count.

THE DEPARTED DAUGHTERS

She was a woman of beautiful voice, and no one could tire of her singing. She was a woman of grace and charm, and no one could tire of her dancing, of the charming grace of her movements. She shook the soa-soa[1] and the timbrels and no one could tire of her music. She taught well the young maidens the dance, made smoothly graceful their movements, taught them the sweet songs to sing, and to shake with their singing the soa-soa. She gave beauty to the less beautiful, and modified plainness wherever she touched, and made finished maidens of the girls in the sande[2]. Before the warriors, the great tribal warriors, she danced to her songs and her music. They applauded her long and called for her often, their best praise went to her of all dancers and singers.

Then the daughter grew up and was like to her mother; her heaven-sent grace the mother well tended, and she became like the mother. True was the copy. And the tribesmen adored her; both mother and daughter the tribesmen adored, and they called for them often for song and for dance, and long they applauded.

[1] (sa'-sa')—An instrument that makes a rattling sound when shaken.
[2] (san'de)—The organization for instructing young women.

127

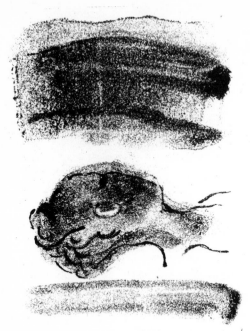

And one day at sunrise the fair daughter spoke and said, "Mother, attend me. I feel faint and ill. I languish with faintness. From whence comes this weakness? I languish with faintness. Give strength to me, Mother. Mother, attend me."

Then the mother tenderly attended her daughter. Trembling with fear she attended her daughter. What was this fear that sat at her heart? She struggled for hope but fear sat at her heart. What could dispel this fear at her heart? What could disperse her daughter's strange illness? Not the medicine man, not the worker of magic, faithfully working. Not the prayers of the mother from sunrise to sunrise. And the mother wept sorely upon the death of her daughter, and the grief of the warriors was mingled with hers. Tears of strong men fell like rain for her daughter, dance and glad song were lost to the mourning, to sad mourning sounds chanting—

> Lost is the maiden, the fair
>   faultless maiden,
> Gone elsewhere to dwell, she is
>   lost to us here.
> Grace-land has sought her, herself
>   was that perfect.
> She has gone to that land. She
>   is lost to us here.

At last the mother said, "I must go back to the sande, back to my work. To live for the dead is grief for the dead, to live for the living is joy for the dead. For the dead are alive to joy and pain. I must live for the living and give joy to the dead." And she went back to the dance and taught the maidens again. And she sought to teach well the daughter of another wife of her husband. She sought to make her a copy of her daughter, that ineffable grace to give to this other maiden, but that could not be. The tribesmen were kind when the maiden danced before them and sang with her music, but she was too plain to please them so greatly.

Then the woman wept again for her daughter departed; she languished again for the daughter departed. Then one night in a dream the daughter appeared and said, "Come down to the water, in the dark hour of midnight come down to the lakeside. Wait for me there in the dark by the water. When first you see me, try not to come to me. I will come to your side, yet try not to hold me, try not to grasp me. Wait for me there in the dark by the water." Then the mother awoke and said, "Can this be so? May the dead visit life? Is a dream but a dream? I'll go down to the lakeside and watch for the dead."

And the next night she did not sleep. She waited for midnight, and time dragged heavy feet, yet she tarried till midnight, then went down to the lakeside, stood alone in the dark and the damp by the lakeside. And at last she heard sounds. Soft symphony sounds, blended with singing, came floating shoreward from over the water. The sounds were from everywhere over the water. How sweet was the singing, how soft was the music! But she moved not, she spoke not, she stood still and listened.

Then suddenly there were lights, soft lights on the water, everywhere. But she moved not, she spoke not. Then suddenly she perceived that each light was a face, each light was not the face but the face was the light. And all shoreward seemed moving, yet none reached the shore. Then from out of the water rose a horse white as snow, came out from the water and stood on the shore, white as the snow. Then a greater light appeared on the water, and that bright light was a face, the bright face of her daughter. And she moved toward the shore to soft, rhythmic music and she rose from the water as shoreward she came. Then she stood by her mother at last on the shore, and the singing and music were beautiful to hear.

Yet the daughter moved not, nor spoke, nor reached for her mother. Then the daughter rose from the ground and sat on the white horse. And all at once the mother felt herself lifted, and she was placed on the white horse by her daughter. Then the horse galloped lightly back to the town, but his feet made no sound. Did his feet touch the ground? Why was there no sound? To her dwelling he galloped and never a sound. Then the horse with the daughter galloped lightly away but his feet made no sound. And the mother alone stood still in the dark till the dark was no more. Then she saw by her side rare stones of great wonder; transformed was her dwelling! Then she opened her throat with a praise-song to Heaven, and the people gathered to hear that glad song. And the song told her story, and her dwelling confirmed it, and the gift of rich jewels. And the people gave her their blessing, they were glad with her gladness, they were filled with her joy.

Then it was that the other wife said to her daughter, "You would do better to die, you please not the tribesmen with your dance and your song. Why do you not die? You could return bearing rich gifts.

Why do you not die?" And the poor girl could not answer, and the mother beat the child till she sickened and died. But none except the mother knew why the child died. Then the mother yearned for the daughter's return, not for the rare gifts she thought the visit would bring.

And then in a dream her daughter came to her, just as the other maiden came to her mother. The same directions were told her as by the other. The next night the mother did not sleep. She went early to the lakeshore, went there and waited and thought that the time never would come. Then she heard sounds out over the water, and she saw lights all over the water. But she did not stand still. She

rushed into the water and grasped the head of her daughter. Then all the faces that were lights went suddenly out and the soft music with them, and the mother stood there with a skull in her hands, and a light like the light of the faces lighted the horrid face of the skull, lighted the grinning face of the white death-skull.

And the woman screamed and made quick to drop the skull into the water, but the skull would not go from her hands. Then the neighbors heard her hysterical shrieking and ran for the lake-shore. What a weird sight they beheld in the dark, the lone woman standing in the edge of the water with the death-skull in her hands. She shrieked till she fell down in the water; and the light of the skull went out, and the sound of shrieking died, and there was only the dark again and the lapping sound of the water. For the skull and the woman were gone and were never more seen in the land. And for years they chanted this song, in a song they chanted the story:

O, the woman that stood in the water,
In the dark and the damp by the sands,
And shrieked in terror at midnight
With the lighted skull in her hands,
And died in fear at midnight
With the death-skull in her hands.

Beware of the water at midnight
In the dark and damp by the sands,
Remember the woman at midnight
With the lighted skull in her hands,
Die not like the woman at midnight
With the death-skull in her hands.

THE GREAT FAMINE

One time there was a great famine in a part of Africa so severe that a great migration occurred, and neighboring states received many temporary refugees. But a few remained in their parched and now desolate homeland, hoping that with reduced numbers enough food would be found to support them. But the food problem became more and more difficult as the famine progressed, and many people and animals perished.

Now in that famished land, not far from the border of a neighboring state where food was still to be found, there was living an eminent spider together with his wife and several children. Perhaps we should say a host of children, since spiders are never known to have a measly few. But in this terrible famine Mr. Spider felt that even one child was really too many, and feeling that way, he had not the courage to count the number he already had. And whenever the thought struck him, as it too often did, that he might well again any day behold his wife, laboriously carrying about with her the visible sign of life, hunger and death all in one bag, he shook violently from the alliance of those dread opposites—fever and chill. Luckily so far, he could still make journeys into the neighboring land and get a supply of provisions, but the journey was long and, with so many mouths to feed, necessity was immediately upon him again. He should have migrated, as his wife urged him to do, but he was loath to leave this home, the ancestral seat of his family for many generations. A home falls into ruin, he argued, if abandoned even for a year or two. He would try to brave it out.

But as time went on, and hunger increased, his self-interest grew enormously. Just as it is with many people—nobody knows, not even they themselves, just how selfish and dishonest they are until faced with necessity. Even the religion they profess loses its necessity to them then, though they may still profess it. But most of them still retain a selfish interest, each one, in his own family. Not so, Mr. Spider. Slyly, by stealth, by subterfuge, and by shameful lying, he cheated wife and children out of the main part of their portion of the food he brought home. He continued in good physical condition, naturally, even though his appetite was never fully satisfied; but his good wife groaned daily at seeing the children decline, and she gave them most of her slender portion, leaving only enough for her bare subsistence.

Now it happened one day that Mr. Spider, while scouting about near his home for something still existing and yet unfound, stopped for rest under a tree whose low-hanging boughs touched the ground all around like a parasol, completely shutting out the sun. "I'll cool off here," he said, kicking his legs to shake some of the sweat from his face. And just at that moment he perceived to his amazement that he was not alone. A turtle, who looked as well fed as Mr. Spider, was also cooling himself there, and was now looking very much frightened.

He had known the dire danger he was in since the moment the spider appeared, and he trembled the more when the spider let out a low triumphant whistle and said, "Halloo, Mr. Turtle! You are a God-send—ordained to prolong my life. Prepare to die. I must sting and stab you to death, good fellow, and later partake of predestined food."

"Wait a minute," said the turtle. "You should by no means sting and stab me to death. I am a God-send, true enough, but you mistake how. I'm sent to do you immeasurable good. Listen. I've trotted around in the shifting shade of your house very much of late and I am grown familiar with your situation and your desire. You wish for means and for seeming good reason to have all the food, your own portion, your wife's, and the children's, for your self-preservation. And under the circumstances you are justified."

The spider stood high with attention. "Speak on, God-sent," he said, so highly pleased thus far that his pleasure gave birth to fear that the turtle might hesitate at the brutal nature of his own proposal and so fail to give the reasons the spider hoped he would give, the reasons why he would be justified in taking all the food from his family.

And the turtle spoke. "You are the strongest of your family," he said. "You are the one most likely to survive when food is all but impossible to find. Better that one live than that all should perish."

"You are right!" exclaimed the spider, slapping the ground so positively he left an impression in the cool, damp soil. "You are indeed God-sent. Nothing could be more apparent, for only a God-sent man can speak as you have spoken. You have thought beyond thought!"

"It is nothing of myself," said the turtle humbly. "I give God the credit."

"Indeed, indeed," cried the spider, "but still you are rarely

blessed, for God does not choose to tell everyone what has been told you!"

"I must concede that," said the turtle, "for the sake of Truth."

"Amen!" exclaimed the spider with increasing fervor, "but I pray you finish this ordained revelation. Light my dark path in these dark times."

"Can you be strong," said the turtle, "can you be unflinchingly strong, remembering that God favors the strong, and see your family starve?"

"For the sake of God, yes," said the spider, "for the sake of God and his ordained will, yes. And after all, under these dire circumstances it would be better for her and the sweetlings to die. It would be better." There was enough pathos in his voice to melt a rock. He tried to say more, but the words stuck in his throat and he gave up the effort.

Then the turtle resumed, as the spider hoped he would do. "Go now and renew your search for food," he said. "You will find something, as you usually have done, and though it be not so much as you wish, it shall henceforth be all yours, so long as God wills. When your wife has prepared the food you have brought in and starts dishing it out, you must stop her and say thus: 'O, wife. The time has come to speak the hard truth. Food is becoming more and more scarce, and now some one member of the family must be given the whole of it, for better it is that one live than that all should perish. God will decide. I shall stand outside the door and call strongly to God for direction. God is just and will answer, and we must submit to his direction. I am willing to perish for the sake of one, yes, for the sake of all if that be possible.' Then you will call and ask whether it is your wife that should have all the food; then whether it is yourself that should live, and last whether it is one of the children whom God has selected to live. I will answer in your favor, and you shall live. If you had stabbed me to death, eventually all of you would have starved; but you never would have stabbed me anyway, for it was ordained that I should live, to point out the means of life to you."

"God be praised!" shouted the spider, slapping the ground again and leaving the second impression of his hand in the cool soil. Then he shook heartily the hand of the turtle and left to look for food, as the God-sent friend had directed.

And he found food, a rather good catch for the day, though far yet too meager for his large family, and his wife prepared it joyously. But as she started to dish it out, he stopped her and gave her the sad, shocking speech of the turtle. But she was quiescent, because she was sincerely religious; and already frantic from seeing the children waste away, she said a silent prayer for the favor of the children. And she felt confident God would favor the children. She waited, trembling, while her husband stepped outside the door of the kitchen hut and called aloud: "O, Great Lord! Hear and give answer. Who is to live while others die? Shall it be my faithful wife?"

There was no answer, and the poor wife breathed freely again and silently thanked God that she was to go for the children's sake, or to go with them. Then he called again and asked if it were he who should live while others died. And clearly through the silence there came the answer: "Whoo-

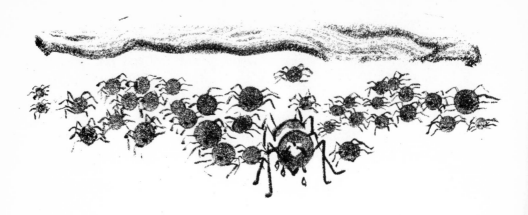

Whoo,"[1] and the poor wife could hardly stand she became so weak. "It is God's will," said the spider, with pathos again in his voice, but pathos did not deter him a moment from eating all the food.

Now after this had been repeated a few days, the wife could bear it no longer. She saw the children piteously withering, and she said to herself, "I myself will go look for food. Maybe God wants me to feed and save the children. Maybe that is it. I will try." And she searched far and near with heartbreaking result, but on the way back to her home, the same tree under which her husband and the turtle had met invited her to a much needed rest, for she was spent from the heat and the long, hard search. You know the turtle was still there; in fact, he had been making the place a temporary home. And when Mrs. Spider saw him, her heart bounded with joy. "Halloo, Mr. Turtle," she said. "You are a God-send. My children shall live yet awhile. It is ordained that by your death my children shall live."

"Hold on," said the turtle, "I am indeed God-sent, and it is ordained that because of me your children shall live, just as you say but not as you think." Then he told her the whole story of his affair with her husband and said further, "It is ordained that through all this your husband shall be brought back to his senses, that the food hereafter will be properly distributed, and all of you survive until better days return, as return they surely will. Now I shall move

[1]Imitation of the Vai word that means *yes*.

140

to another place farther away, and when your husband calls this evening after you have prepared the food, I will answer in your favor. And I'll continue to do so until hunger has forced him to learn that he should divide favors with others who suffer the same need."

Then said Mrs. Spider, "You must indeed be God-sent, for you sound like a God-sent man." And she thanked him sincerely, shook his hand modestly and went home to her children with a new hope in her heart.

That evening Mr. Spider returned with perhaps enough food for himself, but not enough to go round without leaving him hungry. But it was very easy now each day for him to have all the food with false, but seeming good reason. He had but to stand outside the door, call to God, and hear God direct him to eat all the food. But this time when he asked first, as he always asked first, if his wife were to have the food, the voice in the distance answered clearly: "Whoo-Whoo."

"Wait," said Mr. Spider, somewhat startled, "I think God has made an error."

"In that case," said Mrs. Spider, "He has also made history."

"No, no, that is not what I mean," said Mr. Spider nervously. "I mean that I think he has misunderstood the question."

"And that would also make history," said Mrs. Spider drily.

"A God that makes mistakes and a God that misunderstands. What kind of God have we, anyway? I confess I have wondered at times during this awful famine."

"Now, don't question God," said Mr. Spider.

"Who's really doing the questioning, you or I?" said his wife in a wounded tone, which caused her husband to relent with, "Now, now, don't be upset; I'll call again more clearly and God will hear clearly, and, I hope, will answer clearly." Then he called strongly and clearly, and God answered promptly and very clearly. There was no help for it. The wife got the food, and of course she gave

nearly all of it to the children, giving to herself only enough to sustain her with sufficient strength to attend the children. Mr. Spider said he would like to take a walk, and he went promptly to the tree to look for the turtle only to find him gone, and though he searched each day for him here and there he could never find him. But day by day the voice answered in favor of the wife until Mr. Spider himself began to grow weak from hunger, and then his wife felt pity for him, and one day as he lay under a tree in the yard, feeling sick and faint, she said to him, "Maybe God has showed us both the vision of death just to give us a better vision of life. This evening I shall call and ask him if He wants the food divided among all. If God should answer 'Whoo,' then we will know that he have been given a trial for better faith and better deeds, and we will all bear with one another until better days come, as come they surely will."

"You know, Wife," said Mr. Spider with a quiver in his voice, "I think there may be something in what you say. Yes, try that this evening. God does not make mistakes, and God does not misunderstand, but — maybe God sometimes changes his mind." He closed his eyes from weakness and sentiment and so did not see his wife smile as she turned away.

That afternoon she took a short walk and visited the turtle, and both had a mutually good time with their plans for the conversion and reclamation of Mr. Spider. That evening he was despondent from weakness, and the hope of noontime which his wife's remarks had given him was not sufficient at evening. He scarcely stirred when he heard his wife call: "Great Lord! Should we divide the food among us?" But he bounded almost into strength when he heard the clear affirmative answer float in from out of somewhere. Then the good wife served him tenderly as she did the children, and in two days he was bringing in food again, whatever he could find, and

they all subsisted slenderly until better days came to that land, as
come they surely did. And Mr. Spider became prosperous again and
his family was once more happy, but he never again forgot to be
thoughtful of the needs of his family.